fisntank

An Anthology of
New Writing

Introduced by Andrew Motion

Published by the Centre for Creative and Performing Arts, the University of East Anglia.
Typeset in Palatino
Printed by Biddles Ltd
1996 copyright reserved by individual authors.
All rights reserved.

British Library Cataloguing in Publication Data. A catalogue record for this book is available from the British Library.
ISBN 0-9515009-7-X

contents

acknowledgments

Many thanks to Jon Cook, Chris Copin, Emma Hargrave,
Andrew Motion, Mike Oakes, Phoebe Phillips, Richard Johnson,
Anastacia Tohill, and Andy and Vanessa Vargo.
Also, we are grateful for the support from CCPA, and the
Norwich School of Art and Design.

fishtank team
Julia Bell
Susan Gabriel
Sam Goodall
Stephen Finucan
Kate Hardage

Copy editing by Emma Hargrave
Cover design by Chris Copin
Layout by Richard Johnson

A very special thank you to Russell Celyn Jones
and Rob Ritchie.

introduction
Andrew Motion

This anthology is the latest in a series edited, designed and published by members of the Creative Writing MA group at the University of East Anglia, and contains work they have produced during the first two-thirds of the year-long course. The aim, as with previous anthologies, is to gain a wider audience for their writing than can easily be found within the University; the effect is to demonstrate, once again, the vigour, enterprise and ambition of the whole project. The book represents people who are not so much discovering whether or not they can write, as people proving they are poised at the beginning of their lives as writers. Whether the contributions are short stories, extracts from novels-in-progress or filmscripts, they are all marked by a high degree of self-confidence, imaginative energy and commitment.

For the first twenty-five years of its existence, the MA was managed and inspired by Malcom Bradbury. I took over from him in the autumn of 1995, gratefully inheriting the last students admitted under his aegis. In Bradbury's time, voices were frequently raised to challenge the idea that writing could be 'taught'. In my time they have continued to reverberate – feeding on the notion that good writing is necessarily spontaneous, or private, or in other ways unbiddable.

In many respects I agree with these dissenters. I accept that any kind of creativity entails a sense of stealing time, and I also believe that the most successful art draws on parts of the imagination which cannot be treated functionally.

On the other hand, there are many fundamental elements in writing which can be dealt with in the same spirit that a drama teacher teaches acting, or a ballet teacher teaches dance, or an art teacher teaches painting. There is the large business of editorialising, for instance – not just testing each sentence for power and persuasiveness, but addressing questions of narration, characterisation, authorial presence, and so on. There is also the matter of evolving a sense of community. In the weekly workshops at which students present and discuss their work, and in individual or smaller group meetings, course-members are able to share their thoughts in the knowledge that they are talking to kindred spirits. The result is a continuous, evolving lesson about audience, as well as practical or pragmatic issues.

Even supposing the MA students were trying to decide if they were writers at all, this would have its own important purpose. Since they are more properly described as young writers (though not necessarily young in years), it is invaluable. It means that the effort of the course is not to make something from nothing, but to excavate, develop and refine what already exists. To enrich language and association. To broaden the boundaries of the imagination. To explore new ways of reconciling feeling with thinking. To solidify an authentic identity.

All the contributions to this anthology bear witness to the value of the course, and to the qualities of the 'class of 96'. Adventurous and alert, wide-ranging and deep-searching, they will give readers the pleasure of seeing things achieved, as well as the pleasure of sensing things growing.

Andrew Motion
Spring 1996.

Box

Julia Bell

Julia Bell is a vicar's daughter. She was born in 1971 and is currently working on a book of short stories called *Real Girls Eat Meat*. She would like to acknowledge the support of the Tindal Street Fiction Group, Birmingham over the last year.

Life in a box is better than no life at all
Tom Stoppard *Rozencrantz and Guildenstern are Dead*

"Oh fuck," Cindi said, steadying herself against the hosiery rack. "Oh fuck."

She looked at the piece of paper in disbelief. Up the duff at forty-three was not something she had expected.

"Oh FUCK," she said loudly and a few blue rinses turned to stare and tut.

She couldn't possibly have a baby; just thinking about it made her feel claustrophobic. It would ruin everything: her breasts would become immense and pendulous, she'd lose her smooth complexion, and then there was her age, and the show and the stretchmarks, and Pablo would be sure to want to keep it.

She stalked back to the counter, pushing past the old ladies who were huddled in the queue. She had taken her sample to the chemist because it was cheaper than a home test. Now she wished she hadn't chosen somewhere so public.

"This can't be right," she hissed at the assistant who was putting corn plasters in a UniChem bag. She fluttered the piece of paper accusingly. "I've never been pregnant in my life before!"

Until she met Pablo, Cindi's life had been a grey routine of work, sleep and television. Her relationships, like her goldfish always seemed to die after six weeks, and she was, so she thought, heading rapidly for the remainder shelf and a life of solitary, wrinkled misery.

Inadvertently, it was Clark Gable who changed her life. She came home from work one day to find that he had fallen from the wall and that the glass had smashed, fracturing his face into a lopsided grimace. Her heart sank with superstition: falling pictures predicted death and disaster. She hurried into the lounge and lifted the lid of the fishtank. Gordon's silvery belly bobbed on the surface of the water. He had lasted exactly three weeks longer than his namesake.

Whenever Cindi found a new boyfriend, she went to the pet shop and bought a goldfish. She'd heard that they could live to a hundred years, and was determined to make one last longer than six weeks. But it seemed there was always something poisonous in the water. First there was Clive with his mouldy fins, then Barry and Darrien who were poisoned by the duckweed: something to do with DDT apparently. Then there was the virus that sent them banging against the sides of the tank. Colin lost an eyeball before giving up the ghost. It was always the same. After a few weeks of happy equilibrium, navigating the dimensions of her new relationship – going out for meals, drinks, films; enjoying sex on the sofa, in the kitchen, in the garden shed, things always started to stagnate. Scales tarnished, algae crept in green swathes up the sides of the tank, the telephone stopped ringing, and sooner rather than later everything went belly up.

Oh it had all been so easy once, when she was still hopeful. She bought pictures of film stars to hang on the walls – Bogart, Dean, Hudson, Douglas – to remind herself of what she wanted her future husband to look like, knowing that she too, one day soon, would find love, just like in the movies. Fifteen years later they just reproached her with her disappointments. There had been no princes, supermen or movie stars, in spite of the wakeful nights spent in waiting; thrashing the bed sheets into a hot frustrated turbulence about her body. She excelled at nothing, except perhaps carpentry in the fifth year at school and she had an extraordinary knack of killing goldfish. It was ridiculous, she thought reluctantly, as she pulled the chain and sent Gordon round the U-bend into the Stygian waters of the civic drains, after twenty years of trying perhaps it was time to change her approach.

So on a wet windy day in winter, Cindi took two weeks of annual leave and took off in a Jumbo Jet to Torremolinos. She flew up through the clouds and into the sky, searching for Sun, Sea and Sand, and the Magic of Romance.

He was polishing glasses behind the hotel bar, when Cindi walked through the door. He had eyes that shone like freshly-washed dinner plates and a chocolate sundae smile.

"I am Pablo," he said, his plump lips splitting into a grin, "I am to make the cocktails, yes?"

Cindi sat at the end of the bar, watching him deftly mixing and shaking, and chopping up fruit. She studied the undulations of muscle under his shirt and the arrogant swagger with which he presented his drinks. After four Banana Daiquiris and an Orange Orgasmatron her stomach fizzed. This is it, she thought, it's him. At last. She blushed and flustered and spilt her drink everywhere. Pablo grinned and reached out to touch her hair.

"Beautiful Señorita," he said, taking her hand and kissing her fingers.

His touch was electric, sending stars shooting and quivering around her head. She swooned slightly, and wobbled on her stool; she was, she realized, far too drunk.

"Take me to bed," she said, giggling and trying to focus as she draped herself across his arms.

His hands made magic against her skin that night; she tingled and arched and ached, and vanished from consciousness into the slick, slippery casket between her legs. He kissed her neck and mumbled Spanish in her ears. Cindi felt as if she were made of celluloid.

"*¡Voy echar polvo de todas las inglesas viejas!*"

She couldn't understand him, but it didn't seem to matter, he was so young, there was so much for him to learn, and she was sure that his vocabulary would improve once he came to live with her in England.

But when she woke in the morning he was gone. The pillow was dented where his head had been cradled in sleep and there was still a faint warmth in the sheets on his side of the bed. Cindi let a few hot tears escape onto the pillowcase, her heart ached and her head pounded. All that fizzing and quivering last night must have been nothing but the cruel trickery of alcohol. Typical, she thought, clenching her fists, bloody typical.

There was a knock at the door. Cindi jumped and rearranged herself in the bed.

"Come in," she said tremulously, expecting room service. It was Pablo, a tray full of breakfast in his hands.

"Good mornings," he said, his voice muffled by the rose between his teeth, "I comes with breakfast. Soon England I will go with beautiful lady, yes?"

Cindi returned from Spain with toffee in her eyes; she floated through the air-conditioned corridors at work with syrup for brains, wrote torrid letters in her lunch hour even though she knew he couldn't read them, and sent them in envelopes sealed with lipstick. She redecorated her house, and replaced the movie stars with pictures of Spanish scenery: señoritas in red dresses strumming guitars, matadors waving flags for thundering bulls, and vistas of the fiestas in Seville and Madrid. Every night before she slept she would talk to his photograph and imagine that her bed was full with the heavy curves of his body. She plotted and schemed and mooned over brochures in the travel shop, until one day, when spring was bursting with blossom and romance, Pablo finally arrived in England.

Her friends came to the airport, and hissed and cooed and gossiped. He was a bit swarthy they decided, narrow eyes as well – never trust a man whose eyebrows meet in the middle. It was embarrassing to see such desperation: gone soft in the head, at her age, and the boy young enough to be her son. And she knew nothing about him; couldn't even speak the lingo. It wouldn't last, oh no, it wouldn't last.

When she got Pablo home she sat him on the sofa and studied him intensely. She couldn't believe, after the months of longing, that he was finally, really, in her lounge.

"Welcome to England," she whispered as she unbuttoned his shirt.

Perhaps it was the shock of seeing him after all her fevered imaginings, but he wasn't the same as she'd remembered. Slightly smaller, with a more rounded face. In fact, when he'd walked through the arrivals gate Cindi had been unsure whether it was him. When he waved, her heart lifted with relief; it was the same man, she could tell from the smile. It was probably the dull English light that made him look like a stranger. In the dusty heat and burning sun everyone was different, she told herself, as she sucked his earlobe.

Over the following weeks Cindi enjoyed a life of unprecedented sexual adventure. He was exactly what she wanted: young, attractive, male and in her bed; even the goldfish was happy and flourishing. The only problem seemed to be the language barrier. Cindi's grasp of Spanish stretched little further than *Si*, *Rioja* and *castanets*, and Pablo's English wasn't much better. *Hot love lady I want your body* was his most coherent sentence and he'd learnt that from an Italian film. Cindi sent away for an English correspondence course, and while she was at work, she thought of him, crouched obediently beside the stereo repeating conjugations of the verb *to be*.

"We need to find something for you to do Pablo," she said one day, when he had reached book four of *Essential Business English*. "Men are meant to *do* things, it's unnatural you sitting around here all day, and me out to work."

He watched her with his shiny eyes and clicked his tongue.

"We need something you can do so you're not under my feet all the time. Such a big healthy boy like you. You should be out there doing–"

But before she could finish, and suggest that he try gardening, he stood up and started shouting at her in Spanish. She screamed and retreated, terrified, into the kitchen. He was savage and spitting and in a temper, she could hear him grunting and throwing things around in the living room. This is our first argument, she thought, shocked, flicking the switch of the kettle nervously on and off. *Please God*, she whispered to the wall, *please don't let him leave.*

She turned to see him standing in the doorway, penknife in his hand. His eyes were like marbles and a vein stood out on his neck.

"I am Pablo!" he shouted, cracking open the blade and raising his arm. "I am not under a-feets! I am a-dangerous Espanish man!"

Cindi whimpered and closed her eyes. She felt the knife cut through the air and stab into the cupboard behind her head.

She opened her eyes slowly, half expecting to see blood, but Pablo was standing in the doorway with a big grin on his face.

"¡Supremo!" he cried, clapping his hands. "Magic! ¡Voy a hacerme mágico!"

Cindi smiled uncertainly. The knife had missed her by inches. "More like a bloody miracle," she muttered, as he danced a flamenco across the lino to take her in his arms.

"I am Pablo," he said. " I am *mágico supremo*."

At first Cindi pretended not to notice. She would hum to herself and do the cleaning while Pablo watched videos of *The Paul Daniel's Magic Show*. He went to the library and borrowed books: *The Art of Conjury*, *Modern Magic Tricks* and *Successful Sorcery*, and bought rabbits and doves which they had to keep locked in the garage away from the cat.

"Soon I will be famous," was all he would say when she finally questioned him over breakfast one morning, "and can to go España."

Cindi went to work and worried in front of her word processor. He was getting homesick, judging by the amount of letters that he wrote to his mother, and she didn't trust all this dabbling in sorcery. She had visions of returning home to find that Pablo had vanished the cat, or the house, or even worse, himself. She fretted until lunchtime and then left a note on her desk to say that she had gone to the doctor's.

When she got home, Paul Daniels flickered in Pablo's eyes, and his face was ecstatic, full of heroic intent and courageous planning.

"In Barcelona they will to throw flowers and pesetas," he said, turning from the TV to look at her. Cindi didn't know what to say: somewhere along the line she was sure she had lost the script.

"Whatever you want," she said, rummaging in her bag for her knitting.

While she wound her wool into neat spools, Pablo set up the coffee table with tricks and pulled a pair of white gloves over his hands.

"I show to you, my little *paella picante.*" he said, turning the Ace of Hearts into the Jack of Clubs. "I am Pablo. I am a greatest magician!"

His first few tricks were ordinary enough: disappearing coins and pulling ropes of knotted handkerchiefs from the palms of his hands. He vanished a ten-pound note and replaced it with a red carnation, and then a pair of castanets. While he worked he muttered darkly in Spanish, his eyebrows knotting together in concentration.

"*Abracadabra!*" – a rabbit disappeared into a hat. "*Abracadabra!*" it reappeared again as one dove, two, three doves. They fluttered around the living room, settling eventually on the lightshade. Then Pablo put his hand to his ear and produced – orange and flickering against his white gloves – a goldfish.

"Oh Pablo! No!" Cindi squealed, sending the doves flying. Before she could move, Pablo held the squiggling fish by its tail, opened his mouth and dropped it into his waiting gullet. He made exaggerated swallowing noises and then, to Cindi's horror, belched. One of the doves settled on his head and he grabbed it, letting it rest on his hand. *No!* she wanted to say, *fly away!* but the words wouldn't come.

The bird vanished in the flick of a scarf, to be replaced by a glass of water. Pablo looked at Cindi as he lifted the glass to his mouth.

"*¡Salud!*" he said, smiling.

Slowly, very slowly, a tail emerged, still flapping, and then the dorsal fin, and then the whole goldfish plopped out of his mouth and into the glass. Pablo lifted it in the air.

"*¡Mágico!*"

Cindi clapped furiously. "Bravo! Oh bravo!"

That night, she was woken by the sound of sawing. She panicked for a second, imagining thieves, but then registered with dull relief that Pablo wasn't in bed beside her. She put on her pink negligée and padded downstairs.

He was in the living room sawing squares of wood. Doing it all wrong too, she noticed, cutting against the grain like that.

"I am to make boxes! I am–"

Cindi sighed. "I know," she said flatly, "but you're doing it all wrong."

She went up to him and took the saw from his hands. For a moment he hesitated, tugging it back into his grasp. They teetered together, locked in a silent tussle, then Pablo let go with a clenching of teeth and fell on the sofa. Cindi looked at the plan that he'd drawn. It was, she worked out eventually, a blueprint for a long, hinged, magic box that would fold apart in the middle when sawn in half.

"I am to saw halves in the ladies," he said valiantly, "Pablo needs a boxes."

"Go to bed Pablo," she said quietly, "I'll do this."

"No. I am Pablo. I am watchings and helpings."

Cindi roughed her hands against the surface of the wood. It was cheap unseasoned pine, still sticky with sap. The nylon of her negligée snagged as she knelt down to mark out dovetails on the edges of the planks. She took the thick handle of the tenon-saw and with even strokes cut out four identical panels. She smiled as she worked, feeling sweat bubble under her armpit. It was, she suspected now, the lacquered features of the carpentry teacher that had won her attention. Everything at school bemused her except the two hours on a Friday afternoon with Mr Blake. She found something thrilling in Room Five; something that smelled of sawdust and grease, and sounded like the firm rhythm of nails being hammered home.

"I used to do this at school," she told Pablo as she put wood glue in the housings. "I got a prize for my pencil box."

"*¿Qué?*" He looked up from his copy of *The Magician's A–Z.*

"Never mind."

She worked through the night: planing the wood sheer and silvery, honing the joints with sandpaper, chiselling stars and moons in the panels. She measured everything to his specifications, and when it was assembled she covered it in a coat of sticky black paint. Pablo fell asleep over a coin trick, bent over, with his forehead resting on the top of a glass. When the last stroke of paint had been applied, Cindi stood up, wiping her hands on her negligée. She studied her handiwork proudly. Light edged around the curtains and she could hear the rattle of the milk cart outside, radio blaring pop music into the street. She looked at Pablo, his hair flopping onto the coffee table. She poked him awake.

"Look Pablo," she said, as he opened one eye. "I've done it, I've finished. Now what are we going to do with it?"

Pablo sat up and looked at the box. He clapped his hands together. "Now you are to get in, yes?" he said, picking up the saw. "You will be my beautiful assistant."

It's amazing, her friends said when she gave in her notice at work, you never know what she'll do next. It had taken long enough to adjust to the fact that she'd kept a boyfriend – and a foreign boyfriend half her age at that – longer than six weeks, let alone accept that she was throwing it all in for a Bedford caravanette. The woman had surely lost her marbles. A touring magic show? At the seaside? In all their born days they had never heard such preposterous nonsense. No, not never.

*

The curtains opened and Pablo took a deep, flourishing bow. There was weak applause, and as Cindi walked on stage to join him, she saw that most of the seats were still empty. She smiled through clenched teeth, she hadn't the stomach for it today. None of this was part of the plot: the end-of-season shows, the tawdry seaside towns. They were supposed to be in Barcelona where everyone would love them as if they were football heroes – she'd even been taking Spanish lessons. But they'd hardly saved enough money for petrol, let alone plane tickets to Spain. So now here she was, in a crumbling pavillion at the end of the pier, pregnant and sickly, and wishing like crazy she was back at home.

So much for his bloody magic she thought bitterly, as she passed him his wand.

The caretaker set the tape rolling and Pablo began his performance to the soft chords of a Laurindo Almeida guitar solo. He was dressed like a matador, in a starched white shirt and a sequined bolero. He'd left a few buttons open at the neck so the audience could see the curve of his pectorals and the fuzz of his chest hair. Cindi assisted through the first, perfunctory tricks – bringing rabbits out of boxes and doves from the pockets of his jacket – with a glazed ease. Pablo's deceptive hands slipped from one routine to the next, while Cindi cracked her face with smiles and tried to sparkle when she faced the audience.

It would probably have been all right, had she not been in such turmoil. Her stomach tingled as if someone had punched her and now that she knew, she could feel it: growing in her belly like a maggot.

The music changed to Tchaikovsky's *1812* Overture and Pablo wheeled the box to the centre of the stage.

"Now!" he shouted, "I am sawing the lady in halves. I am Pablo. I am a greatest magician!"

Cindi faced the audience and dropped a curtsy as he opened the lid. She had to act sad and terrified, which wasn't too difficult today. Pablo pretended after a mock tussle, to capture her; his arms round her waist, his lips on her cheek. She went through the motions of smiling and relenting, allowing herself to be led to the box. She stretched, raising her arms in the air in a balletic gesture and then stepped in the box, sitting down slowly, keeping her back straight and her arms in the air as she bent her knees. When she was sitting down, she turned to the audience and waved.

Pablo shut the lid and whirled the box around on its castors. As it spun, he opened his big red bag and took out six silver swords and a big shiny saw. He held the saw above his head and bent it like a strongman bending an iron bar. The crowd oohed and aahed, and leant forward in their seats to see Pablo sawing the lady in half.

Once inside, Cindi had to move quickly. Lying on her back inside a spinning box, she folded her legs up so her knees touched her breasts and her shins were pressing against the lid. Contorted like this, so that half the box was empty, she waited for Pablo to start thrusting swords through the holes chiselled out in the stars and moons.

The first scorched under her ankles. One down, and she could let her feet rest on the blade. The next flew through the very small gap between her thighs and her stomach. She shivered and held her belly in. She could hear Pablo, his pumps squeaking against the boards of the stage, his movements synchronised with the music. The third sword, and the fourth, rattled into the empty half of the box. Cindi took a deep breath, she hadn't even been sawn in half yet.

Pablo brandished the final sword and thrust it through the end of the box. He spun the whole contraption round so that the audience could see all the swords buried up to the hilt, their points sticking out on the other side.

Of course she wasn't really in the box, the audience said, whispering about trapdoors and mirrors. It was all a trick, they knew that, they weren't even the slightest bit worried that there might be a mutilated lady inside.

Then Pablo took the saw and made huge choreographed sawing actions. When he was done, he split the box into two halves, so that the gasping audience could see that there was no body between the gap. The woman must have escaped. No one could be alive in there.

Cindi felt her muscles cramp with tension. After all that spinning she felt dizzy, and the little grub inside her was fattening and making her sick. It wouldn't be long before it clawed its way out; inching through her intestines, snaking up through her stomach, until it came spewing out of her mouth like Pablo's goldfish trick. She swallowed, trying to keep it down. Whatever she did, it would come between them now. Cindi heard the tapping of the wand, which meant that Pablo would be taking his swords out soon. The audience went quiet with anticipation. Cindi took another deep breath and listened. Every second, the heartbeat in her belly was gaining in power and certainty. It radiated through her like fever, making the ends of her fingers and the tips of her toes throb uncomfortably. She felt a surge of panic. She was changing, without a doubt, she was changing.

With his magic wand Pablo tapped on the lid of the box three times in ceremonious succession. Then he carefully drew out the swords. The audience looked for blood, but the blades were as clean and shiny as when they went in. There was a drum roll, and the music changed to Vivaldi's *Spring*. Pablo opened the box, pretending, with extravagant gestures to be a Prince Charming come to wake his Sleeping Beauty. The audience craned their necks and stood on tiptoe.

Pablo let out a cry of surprise and reached into the box. *Oh no!* the audience said to themselves, *it must be an accident, look he's crying*. And sure enough Pablo's eyes were streaming with tears as he pulled a bundle out of the box. He turned to face them, holding the baby close to his chest and opened his mouth as if to speak, but the words seemed choked in his throat.

Whispers passed round the audience. *What a clever trick! How extraordinary! She must have escaped into a trapdoor. Bloody marvellous magic* – and they broke into an applause so impressed and thunderous, that it deafened their ears, and no one noticed that the child in the magician's arms was wailing at the top of its lungs.

They clapped so hard and cheered so loud that it rattled the roof, sending a flock of starlings that were nesting under the guttering flying into the air. Terrified wings rose above the pier in a cloud, hovered for a second, then dispersed like the bloom of a firework into the deepening dark of the evening sky.

Extract from

The Trial of Noble West

Stephen Finucan

Stephen Finucan, born in 1968, is from Toronto. He would like to dedicate his work in this anthology to his grandparents, Harold and Grace Price.

ONE: First Things First

My name is Noble West. Seventy-four years ago I was pushed into this world in a bedroom above my grandparents' pub, the Tom o' Bedlam. It was a big day for my mother. Moments before she fell into her one and only labour, news came that her husband, the Jack that was my father, was dead. The purple-inked form letter, which was how they did such things back in 1915, said the sad event took place somewhere in France or Belgium. The military was wary of giving any definite location – loose lips sink ships. The only thing that seemed certain was that it had been the Germans who killed him.

Anyhow. So there she was, a brand-new war widow on the verge of becoming a mother. I'd say that's enough to knock anyone off kilter. Which could explain the strangeness of my name. I was supposed to be a Jack, too. I haven't a clue what my mother was thinking when she stuck me with this handle. Her dead husband maybe; her poor, brave, honourable, dead, soldier husband. Or maybe she had visions of gallant knights, who knows. Of course, to hear my grandmother tell the story, which she did five years later, the explanation was far simpler: my mother was none too bright.

I think that part of her rubbed off on me. All I have to do is take a look around me to realize that I'm not the sharpest knife in the drawer. I've done some stupid things, but this tops it.

I came in here three days ago with my ass on fire. I could hear the nurse coughing as they wheeled me through the corridors. They had to waft the smoke away before they could cut off my trousers and shorts. I don't know if the Germans have something against my family, but after they pulled away my underwear – along with a good

23

chunk of skin – the doctor seemed pretty happy about sticking a foot-long pin in my rump. Near as I can tell, he only did it to make me scream. I was happy to oblige.

None too bright is what my grandmother said. Well, none too bright is how I feel.

I have only one memory of my mother. I am four years old, which makes her about twenty-two. I am lying on the floor of the wash-house out back of the pub. My mother is floating above me.

It's a nice recollection, dreamy like. Although the rope around her neck does take away from the effect. Still, I suppose it was lucky for me that she was no deft hand at tying a noose. Otherwise, I would've been floating there beside her, rather than lying on the floor looking up.

I suppose it was lucky for me – funny that. Here I am with a pillow rammed under my hips and my bare ass stuck in the air for all to see. And I don't move for fear I'll crack the scabs again and send the pus dripping back into my wound. Not much *lucky* in that. Come to think of it, there really isn't anything funny about it either.

I'm sure the police are getting a kick out of it, though. They've been here as long as I have. There's always one sitting by the door, watching me. As if at any moment I'm going to make a dash for it. My shitter's covered in blisters, for Christ's sake. I can't even walk. Forget walk, I can't even fart without howling in pain. Besides, I'm tired of running. I won't do it anymore. If they want me that badly, they can have me. They can put me back in prison for all I care. Hell, if they got a mind to, they can even try hanging me again.

They're going to ask me to explain myself soon, I can feel it. I mean, it's been three days already. And it's not like they can't find someone who speaks English. Not nowadays. I'll bet that even that nasty woman who takes so much pleasure ripping off my old bandages can *sprechen sie Englisch*. No doubt she puts my *Deutsch* to shame.

Of course, none of this is going to make a lick of difference if I don't have my story straight. But it's hard remembering things in their proper order. Memory isn't like that, it jumps around like a flea. As soon as you think you've squashed it, it turns around and bites you somewhere else. One minute I'll be thinking of my sweet Mary in the safe-house outside Dublin, then suddenly she's older and pointing her gun at me under the Arc de Triomphe. But these things, these Marys, are years apart. And when I try to sort them out, I end up with the young Mary holding the gun and the old Mary holding me. And that's not right, either.

The easiest thing is to walk through it from the start. To go back to 21 September 1919: the day I looked up from the wash-house floor. For me that's it, that's my beginning. The dirty soles of my mother's feet welcomed me into the world. The dear woman strung me up on my fourth birthday. And while she didn't succeed in killing me, she did a pretty fair job at erasing the first three years of my life. I can't say for sure what happened to those forty-eight months. I guess I left them dangling from the crossbeam, along with my poorly tied noose. And my mother, whom I no longer knew.

I'm sure I did when I stepped onto the over-turned wash-tub with her and she slipped the rope around my neck. But by the time that knot unfurled, she was a complete stranger to me. I went up onto that wash-tub a half orphan and came down a full one.

I must have had some inkling back then of what my world would be like. Not anything definite, but enough for me to want to keep my eyes shut a good deal of the time. I would've been wise to have kept them closed for a lot longer than I did.

The second time I was dumb enough to open them, I found myself staring at the ceiling of the room in which I'd been born. And I would have been happy with just that: an off-white, cracked plaster ceiling. But I've rarely got what I wanted in my life – and I didn't then, either. What I was given was a fat, blubbering face.

Enter my grandmother: Netty Mahon.

No sooner did I see her dripping kisser, than she fell on top of me and began to squeeze so hard I couldn't breathe. I heard a voice after that. Unfortunately, I couldn't see who owned it because my eyes were full of hair. But here's what it said:

"Give over, Netty. You'll end up finishing what his mother started."

What a terrible thing to say. That kind of stuff can permanently scar a kid. It's just lucky I didn't know what they were talking about. As it was, the only scar I ended up with healed fairly well. It's not much more than a slightly puckered grey ring that passes under my chin, and my beard covers that.

I wonder if they'll shave my face. I wouldn't think so, considering it's my ass that's causing all the trouble. They've already shaved down there. They did it just before they stuck the tube up my prick. No matter. When you've got no dignity, you've got no dignity to

Stephen Finucan

lose.

That voice that seemed to care so little about wounding my fragile psyche belonged to Dr Hartoper. So did the big, vein-lined, pit-covered nose that pretty near took my eye out after my grandmother finally let go of me. To say that nose was the worst thing I'd ever seen wouldn't mean much, since all I really had to compare it to was Netty's sloppy face.

I don't know how Hartoper came to be called a doctor, except that he owned a stethoscope. The fact was, he was no different from anyone else who lived on Holly Street – or in the rest of the Jewellery Quarter for that matter.

That's where I lived, the Jewellery Quarter. It's in Hockley, which has always been one of the more unattractive boroughs of what many people consider the strikingly unattractive city of Birmingham. The last time I was there, which is going on fifteen years now, there wasn't much left of the old neighbourhood except a couple of the pubs – of which the old Tom o' Bedlam wasn't one. Other than that, it's mostly factories and warehouses; some might say that that's an improvement.

During the time I was there as a child it was a dingy, smog-filled slum. Nothing jewel-like about it at all. The back-to-backs that crammed every street were held together by the foundry soot that clung to everything, including the little wooden cross stuck into the ground beside the wash-house. I'm sure the soot would have clung to the trees and grass too, if there'd been any. Instead, there were cobblestones. They covered the streets, the lanes, the yards, everything.

It was called the Jewellery Quarter because that's what got made there. Shiny things like gold and diamond rings, burnished brass buttons and beadsteads. Not that any of it stayed in the Quarter. No one there could afford to buy it. They could scarcely spare the price of mutton. Most of them had to rely on the Parish Relief to get enough to feed themselves and their families, which usually numbered about ten – and that's a lot of mutton.

Of course, we weren't so badly off. We ran the local. Sure, we had to put up with same choking smoke from the foundries – and anyone can catch lice – but at least our toilets were bearable. Those poor bastards in the groves had to line up just to take a shit. And let's face it, everybody's shit stinks, but when you've got thirty people dumping in the same box, the aroma tends to be that much more rosy.

Now that I think about it, Doc Hartoper was probably doing okay, too. Whether he was a real doctor or not didn't seem to make much difference to anyone in the neighbourhood. He had his stethoscope and he was cheap: a shilling a visit. And he didn't ask questions. His fee never changed, either. It didn't matter if it was a canker or consumption, both of which were rampant, it was still a shilling. It wasn't like he could do a hell of a lot, but at least he didn't judge people. Which is more than I can say for the doctors at the district clinic, who put everything down to cleanliness. I guess they didn't hold much faith in the power of carbolic soap.

I liked Hartoper. His hands were cold and clammy. He wrapped them around my neck while I was looking at his ugly nose. I didn't realize how sore the rope-burn was until he did that; his fingers were like ice. God, it was wonderful. I wish he were here now – although, I don't think he'd be too happy about applying his cool touch in this case.

After he let go of my throat, he walked to the far side of the room and stuffed his stethoscope into the hessian bag he always had slung over his shoulder. Then he whispered something to Netty and looked back at me and grinned.

"Stay in bed and you'll have no worries," he said.

Now there's some advice that hasn't stood the test of time. Here I am, lying in bed, and all I've got are worries. And that shrew with the bedpan knows it. I swear I can hear her giggling every time she rams the suppositories between my burning cheeks.

I'd give anything to know what Hartoper was grinning about that day. He was a weird old bugger. You never knew what went on in that head of his. Maybe when he turned around and looked at me he saw it all. Knew, then and there, how it was going to pan out. If that's the case, I can't blame him for having a little chuckle.

But the thing that bothers me so much is that Hartoper never smiled at anything. As well as being all queer and mysterious, he was a grim bastard. He rarely parted his lips for anything besides whisky. He was about as talkative as Poppy, whom I hadn't met yet.

Enter my grandfather: Poppy Mahon. I met him on my second day – though *met* might not be the word for it. He was tall and rake-thin, with salt and pepper hair that sat up on his head in a shock. He was standing on the far side of the bedroom, rolling a cigarette and smiling. That's pretty well all he did the whole time I knew him: rolled cigarettes and smiled. I'll never forget how he did it. He'd line the baccy in the palm of his left hand and lay the paper on top of it. Then, with a quick flip, like he was doing a magic trick, he'd shift the lot into the fingers of his right hand. And he'd roll up the fag with just that one hand. I've never been able to do it. Every time I try, I end up spilling perfectly good tobacco down my front.

There's not much more to say about him. Except maybe that he and Hartoper were a cut of the same cloth – opposite sides, mind. Poppy was pleasantly indifferent, whereas Hartoper leant more toward the unsavoury.

I haven't said anything about bombs yet. That's hard to believe. It seems like they've been there every day of my life. I'd almost forgotten there was a time before them; a time before Farini.

But I mustn't jump ahead. As it stood, I didn't even know my name yet.

For a time, I thought I was called Jane. I blame Netty for that. She was smothering me again, rocking back and forth, even though the slightest movement of my head sent burning waves of pain through my neck. Hartoper told her as much, not that she ever paid attention to him. I was supposed to be left alone to rest. But as I recall, every time I opened my bloody eyes, Netty was there blubbering away.

You'd think she was a weepy old cow, the way she acted. But I learned early that grief is a temporary state. In those first days, when I looked into that frighteningly ugly face of my grandmother – all plump and jowly, criss crossed with thin ruddy veins, flapped and folded with mushy wrinkles, and topped off by big caterpillar eyebrows that came together almost half way down her pugilist's nose – I felt something akin to sympathy. She was very much in despair. And when the time came that she wasn't, all those podgy features became downright hard. And her weepy voice turned icy-sharp .

But that time hadn't come yet. Then, her voice was still soppy; and very close to my ear.

"Oh my baby," she snivelled. "My poor sweet Jane."

What was I supposed to think? She was holding me, so naturally I assumed I was Jane. I had no way of knowing that she was moaning about my mother. And it really wouldn't have made any difference if she'd told me.

What Netty did next didn't help matters. She shifted to my other ear and slobbered:

"Oh my baby. My poor sweet Noble."

It was only through the process of elimination that I was finally able to figure out which of these names was my own.

It still amazes me how tough Netty became afterwards. She is easily the hardest woman I've ever met – and I've met a lot. This nurse who's *looking after* me could probably give her a run for her money, but she'd still lose out in the end. If I had a choice between Frau Mengele taking care of my ass or dear old Netty, I'd take my sweet Aryan Nightingale every time. There've even been women who've wanted to kill me, and I'd still take them over Netty. And she was my gran, for Christ's sake.

Maybe that's why Poppy never said or did much. Netty wouldn't let him. She sailed the ship that was the Tom o' Bedlam. In the whole time I was with my grandparents, I only saw her lose one argument. It was with Poppy. And even then it wasn't a true argument. But considering what happened after that one, I doubt she ever gave into him again.

Well, there. I've just told my first lie. The truth is there was one other argument I saw Netty lose. It was with the priest.

I remember I was getting stiff from being in bed, so I got up and wandered over to the window. Netty was out front of the pub. She had her hands clasped in front of her, and she was shaking them. I couldn't quite make out what she was saying, but the tone of her voice struck me as odd. The only word I can come up with to describe it is womanly, and I know that's not right. The priest didn't say anything. He just stood there shaking his head. Then he walked away.

That's why Poppy had to pull up the cobblestones out beside the wash-house. Because my mother had taken her own life, the priest refused her a grave in the church cemetery. So my grandfather dug her one out back.

I don't much like men of the cloth. I'm sure some quack would put it down to the fact that the first priest I ever saw denied my mother the decency of a Christian burial. But that's got nothing to do with it. I'm not a Christian. And as for the denigration of my mother's body, well, Poppy could've dug that hole to hide a bone. That's how much I cared.

No, my dislike for priests resides on a much more basic level than that. It's this idea they have that they're different from everyone else. This godliness thing, I don't buy it. I've come across many a clergyman in my day, and I can vouch for their sameness. They'll stab you as quickly as a crook, sometimes quicker.

I almost ran into my mother again, before they planted her in the back garden. It was the day after Netty lost her argument with the priest. I was getting a little tired of the bedroom, and there was a crazy racket coming from downstairs. So I figured, what the hell.

My first view of the pub didn't last more than thirty seconds. Everything stopped – talking, drinking, laughing, crying – when I walked into the bar. And before I even had the chance to get a good look at what was standing in the corner, Dr Hartoper had a hold of me and was marching me back down the hallway, up the stairs, down the other hallway and back through the bedroom door.

Without a word, he tucked me back under the bedclothes and poured a whole cup full of sherry – which he used to administer in small doses to help me sleep. He waited as I drank the lot. Then he took the cup away, and left the room. I heard him turn the key in the lock.

That was the first Irish wake I ever went to. There would be others. Danny McGrath's and Declan O'Maonlai's in Wicklow. And, of course, the Mick's back in Orton. But they were still years away.

I'm not sure why Hartoper hustled me out the pub so quickly. Maybe he thought I'd upset everyone else – like I'd be a reminder of how terrible the whole situation was. Or maybe he was thinking of the effect it would have on me. What's more likely is that he didn't want a little spit like me putting a damper on the festivities.

Christ, what a start. Four days, that's how long all that took. Four bloody days. It's a wonder that it took me another twenty-five thousand nine hundred and eleven to blow myself to bits. But, as Farini would say, all in good time.

TWO: With a Bang

Those first few days aside, the time with my grandparents was pretty much uneventful. Soon after I came down from the bedroom, my life fell into a tedious routine which Netty ruthlessly enforced. Every morning at seven, I had to light the scullery fire so I could have her tea ready for when she came downstairs. This involved my going into the cellar and bringing up enough slack for the day.

The cellar was a foul place. The damp dripped from the walls and the ceiling. Overflow from the ale and bitter kegs had soaked into the earthen floor and its skunky stench was nauseating. And the rats that lived down there were bigger than my head. They were cocky buggers too! – standing about on the barrels or coal-tip, watching me with those beady yellow eyes.

There's not a lot that bothers me, but those bastards sure as hell do. During that year I stayed with Netty and Poppy, I used to dream about them. I dreamt that they came up from the basement during the night and skittered their way into my bedroom. Then, while I slept, they would crawl up under the blankets and begin to gnaw at the raw flesh that ringed my neck. I can't remember the number of times I woke up gasping for air, only to find I'd been lying there strangling myself.

That dream came back to me during the war, while my unit was moving through Amsterdam. I saw a corpse floating in one of the canals. It was so bloated the only way you could tell it was a body was by the hands, they stuck up from the sides at right angles. But that's not what started the dream again. I mean, that was 1944, and I'd seen plenty of dead folk by then. No, what started it again was what I saw coming out of the corpse's mouth: a fat, grey, water-soaked rat.

I never told Netty that I was afraid of the cellar-rats. I can't imagine she'd have been overly sympathetic. It didn't take long for me to realize that there were two Nettys: upstairs and downstairs.

The upstairs Netty was drippy, rubbed-red nosed and puffy-eyed. And once I joined the world of the downstairs Netty, that one who'd squeezed my cheeks, pawed my hair and pulled me into her great heaving bosom ceased to exist; she was replaced by one who yelled.

In the morning, when she wanted her tea, she yelled. When she saw empty pint glasses sitting on the tables, she yelled. If one of the punters had fallen asleep, pissed his pants, or puked up his last ale, she yelled. Her constant bellowing ensured that Poppy and I stuck to our routines.

Aside from collecting the coal every morning, I also had to fetch water from the standpipe outside the back door. This wasn't too bad during the warm months, but come January and February, I usually had to bring a burning piece of ale crate with me and run it up and down the spout to thaw the ice. Which meant I had to get up even earlier.

Then came breakfast, usually bread and dripping. After which I polished the taps. Netty demanded that they be shiny enough for her to see her face. God knows why.

The pub opened at eleven, and served bread and cheese until three. During that time my jobs were many: hauling full plates from the scullery and empty ones back, bringing bottles of ale from the rat-filled cellar and spirits from the storage room upstairs, and keeping an eye on Poppy. Netty wanted to be informed every time he gave out a free pint or poured one for himself.

This last job continued during the evening hours, when Netty stopped serving food in favour of drink only. I can honestly say that I did not perform this task with any vigilance. There were two reasons for this: first, I disliked this new version of my grandmother so much that I was happy to let her husband deceive her; second, every time Poppy saw me witness his little thieveries, he slipped me a lump of sugar to keep my mouth shut.

I don't blame Poppy for much that happened to me in my life, mainly because he did so little. But the one thing I do hold him responsible for are my horrendous teeth. So often did he fill that chipped enamel cup of his, or slip a complimentary measure to Dr Hartoper, that my baby teeth rotted from my head well before their time. And when my permanent ones finally made their appearance, the sweet-tooth that he had nurtured made their survival an impossibility.

The result of this is that I've had dentures for most of my adult life. Except now. I lost them in the blast. The force of it not only blew my rear inside out, it also sent the old teeth a-flying. So, while I lie here, gumming my way through this sad story, my teeth are out there on some *strasse* or other.

Last Orders at the Tom o' Bedlam was eleven, and Netty made sure that all drinks were off the table by half-past. This was one of the only things she enjoyed doing on her own. And even though the same complaints were raised by the same customers, only once did I see anyone decline to hand over their pint when she came collecting. It was a young navvy who'd been working with a crew down along the canal. The lot of them had been in every night for about a week, and they always asked to be locked in. Netty always refused. When Friday rolled around, and again she said no, this lad stood up and told her that he and his mates would leave when they were good and ready.

Plenty of people had voiced their displeasure to Netty before, but none had ever actually stood up to her. So when this shaver – who was no thicker than a wick – did, those still left in the pub took notice. And each one of them, myself included, knew that the navvy had made a mistake when he turned to smile at his chums. No sooner had his lips split into a grin than Netty did the same to the back of his head with a bottle. He dropped like a wet cloth.

It was my job to clean up the glass and blood that was left behind when the rest of the crew dragged their whimpering friend into the night. We didn't see them again after that.

But as hard as Netty was, I only ever saw her violent twice. The navvy was the first. The other was Farini. Everyone else steered clear of her.

Sundays were pretty much an off-day at the pub, for me at least. I only worked until two. At which point I got a boot in the rump from Netty, who told me to get out from under foot.

I spent fifty-four Sundays with my grandparents. And all but one I spent in my bedroom looking out the window, watching the residents of Holly Street go about their business.

That one time I did go out, I followed some kids I'd seen from my window. They'd just pulled apart an orange crate that the shopkeeper across the way had left out. I trailed a good distance behind as they made their way back down Holly Street, dragging their pieces of wood along the cobblestones. At the groves they turned and went into one of the yards. I don't know why they called those crumbling back-to-backs groves, or why they called the yards yards for that matter. Those names are too quaint for what these places were: tumble-down tenements built with dodgy material by skimping contractors and run by money-grubbing landlords, crammed so close together that the twenty families living in each terrace may as well have been in each other's laps.

Anyhow, I stopped beside the rubbish heap at the top of the yard and watched the other children. They huddled together and sharpened their sticks on the cobbles. Then they formed a ragged skirmish line across the width of the yard, and began to move slowly toward the dividing wall at the far end. I've seen this manoeuvre used since. It was a favourite of the Americans. When we met up with them across the Dutch border, outside a small town called Geilenkirchen, they employed the same strategy to try and cross the fields that surrounded the town. Unfortunately, the tall grass concealed the maze of German trenches. Four hundred GIs died before they called for air support.

It's too bad the cat at the far end of the yard didn't have the same cover as the Germans. I stood there and watched it try to hop up onto the wall. It didn't help that it already had a limp. And by the way it was pacing, it was obvious it had been through this before. The thing howled like a baby when they pinned it to the cobbles with their slivers of orange crate. Then, the smallest kid snatched it up by the scruff of the neck and raced into one of the bogs. I heard one more howl before he dropped it into the cesspit.

The kid saw me when he came out of the latrine and stopped laughing. The rest of them waited beside the gas-lamp as he came down to where I was. He stood in front of me and scratched his head with the pointy end of his stick. Then he cleared his throat and spat a great green gob on my shoe.

"I know who you are," he said.

I just stared back at him. His hair and skin were as dusty as the cobblestones, and he shifted back and forth, midway between a giggle and a sneer.

"You're the bastard," he said. "Your mam kilt herself. Strung herself up."

Then he took a step forward and swung. The stick caught me on the side of the head. When he pulled back to hit me again, I ran. At first there was only one set of footfalls pounding out behind me, then the others joined in. They were much faster than I was – being practised hunters and all – and I was caught half-way between the groves and the pub. First came a push that knocked me to the ground, followed by sticks and feet.

A familiar voice stopped everything. After that I heard the slap of a hand across a face, but I didn't open my eyes until the footsteps had faded back down the street. When I did, I was looking into that big, vein-lined, pit-covered nose again.

"You look alright to me," Dr Hartoper said.

He lifted me to my feet, pulled something out of my hair, then carried on his way to the pub. I tried to stay in step with him. He was quiet until we reached the pub, then, without looking at me, he said:

"What was that about?"

I didn't know, so I asked him what a bastard was.

After my run-in with the urchins, I spent those half-days in my bedroom, watching the little shits from a safe distance. They would stand across the street, at the shop, and make faces at me. And when no one was watching, they'd gather stones and throw them at my window.

And I did bugger all. Unless you could call standing there like the village idiot doing something.

That's how I spent most of my year at the Tom o' Bedlam. But as August pushed on to September, things began to change. We were rapidly approaching the only other argument I would ever see Netty lose. The one with Poppy.

He began it innocently enough on the first of September with these words:

"It's the boy's birthday in three weeks."

He repeated this statement, with the obvious alterations, everyday for a week. And when he reached: "It's the boy's birthday in two weeks," Netty finally countered.

"You think I don't know that," she bellowed. Then added: "You drunken fool."

Poppy just smiled and rolled a cigarette. I stood on an ale crate behind the bar, shining the bitter tap, and watched. Netty began to seethe. She'd been tossing new sawdust onto the floor, and I could see her clenching and unclenching her fist inside the burlap sack. Her face grew flushed as she waited for Poppy to say something else.

When he didn't, she blurted out: "Oh, for God's sake. What of it?"

Poppy flipped the cigarette into his mouth and calmly lit it. He took two long drags before he answered.

"I thought we might do something special for the lad."

That was the day I first heard the name Farini. I've known two since then, but the second paled in comparison to the first. It's the first one that I like to think of as my mentor. He changed my life. True, it wasn't always for the better. But I guess you've to take the spit with the shine.

If Netty'd had her way – and to this day I don't understand why she didn't – Farini would never have entered my life. But Poppy wore her down. Through all the screaming and swearing, the fury and fuss, he persevered. Each morning for the next week and a half, he repeated his position. I came to expect it. As soon as I put my cloth to the bitter tap, he'd speak. Then Netty would launch into stinging profanity.

Then one day she didn't. I stopped my polishing and Poppy stopped his rolling, and we looked at her. She'd been defeated. That's the nearest she ever came to looking like the upstairs Netty downstairs.

"Fine," she said, and laid her rag on the table. Then she walked past the bar, down the hallway, and out the back door toward the wash-house.

The Great Farini arrived at mid-morning on my fifth birthday. As chance would have it, he burst through the door just as I set my cloth against the bitter tap. The sun that day was extraordinary – even in the Jewellery Quarter – and it shone through the doorway like a gem. A gem with a wiry flaw running through its centre.

When he stepped out of the glare, I got my first glimpse of the magician. He was short, unwashed, unshaven, and had a glimmering gold tooth that flashed when he smiled. I'll never forget his first words:

"De Greata Farini needsa stout."

I stood there, awe-struck on my ale crate. He had such a wonderful, strange voice, deep and rich. Not like the lazy nasal inflections of my fellow Brummies. He said he was Italian. It wasn't until years later that I found out he was, in fact, a native of Cromer. The closest he'd ever come to being Italian was through his father, who'd once been a cook on a Spanish merchant ship.

He swallowed the pint Poppy set out for him in one swift gulp, then slammed the glass down and let out an enormous belch.

"Nuttin' better for-a empty stomach," he said. "Now, I'lla be outta you hair til itsa time for de show."

Then he turned and looked sternly at me. With a slow hand he reached behind my ear and pulled it back to reveal nothing. I'd heard the small stone he'd held in his closed fist drop onto the floor behind the bar. He seemed confused, then shrugged and said:

"No matta."

He turned and started out of the pub. Just before he reached the door he spun around and looked at me again.

"I'lla need a assistant. You donta know where I canna fine one?"

I spent the whole of that day ferrying empty pint glasses to the bar and full ones back to Farini, while he set about building his stage out by the wash-house. It was really no more than a square frame with a makeshift curtain hung from the crossbeam. The curtain itself, which was a tattered old bedspread, was a deep purple and had faded yellow stars scattered loosely across it. The tears in it, and there were many, were sewn carelessly with white stitching. The whole thing was a shambles, but I didn't care – to me it was absolute magic.

I had a hat like that curtain once: purple with stars. It was a baseball cap I picked up in some shithole nowhere town near Boise or Butte. I was through so many of those crappy little hovels in the mid-seventies. It was before we got the call to go to Vegas, I know that much.

I carried cups for Farini until the sun began to set. Even though he'd finished putting up the stage by half-four, he made me promise not to say anything to Poppy. So, I didn't.

After he'd finished setting up, Farini spent the rest of the day lying on his red and green and yellow trunk, sipping stout and humming softly. When the kids from the grove started poking around, he threw a rock at them and told them to piss off.

It wasn't until a little after eight that he sat up and said:

"Right. Go an a tella de landlord I'm a ready."

The far end of the yard was already crowded with punters when I stepped out from behind the curtain. Poppy was serving them bottles through the outdoor and I could hear Netty yelling at the customers inside. When the shout went up that the magician was ready to start, the people pushed themselves into a mob and surrounded the stage. And five minutes after that, The Great Farini emerged, a long, stained cape draped over his shoulders. Everyone laughed as he made an unsteady bow. He didn't speak, but moved about the improvised stage, making wide sweeping gestures with his spindly arms.

His magic was sloppy. Poorly hidden flowers materialized from behind grubby handkerchiefs. Cups and saucers disappeared into pockets in his cape, only to peak out again when he shifted too quickly. Cards slipped from his sleeve when he passed an empty hand across the deck. People began to get restless. Jeers came from different areas of the crowd. Someone threw a half-eaten apple that passed by his head and hit the curtain without him noticing it.

Finally, just as the mob was building to a frenzy, he vanished behind the curtain. Some people swore and hurled empty bottles at the bedspread; others muttered their way back into the pub. It seemed to take forever for Farini to re-emerge. When he did, he was dragging a small crate behind him. It was muddy-brown and splintered. He shifted it carefully on the ground, and when he was satisfied with its positioning, stepped in front of it. Then he turned back to the angry crowd and spoke for the first time.

"Now we see who-a laugh atta De Greata Farini."

He pulled two short, red sticks from the pocket of his cape and held them aloft. From another pocket he produced two wicks and waved them high, as well. The punters grew quiet.

The care he took in inserting the wicks was almost painful, but no one made a peep. The job done, Farini held the sticks above his head once again. Then, with lightning quickness, he drew a match from another pocket and struck it against his boot. The fizzle, spark, and flame seemed to frighten the onlookers.

Farini held the burning match close to his face. While everyone was watching the match, he lifted the lid of the crate with his foot. In another speedy motion, this one even quicker than the first, he lit the wicks, dropped the sticks into the crate, closed the lid, and sat himself down on top of it.

That was the moment I fell in love with bombs.

Extract from

The Counting of
Flowers

Susan Gabriel

Susan Gabriel lives and is grateful.

Writer's Note: By the time the reader reaches the following extract from my novel-in-progress, they will be aware that Munro and Clara are the farmer and his wife who lived in Trethella, a Cornish farmhouse, one century before Howard and Sara, the present occupants. They will also recognize Luke as someone from Sara's past, the memory of whom both comforts and haunts her.

"Look, Howard," Sara calls, peering into an outhouse crammed full, "that's a rocking chair, isn't it?" The arch of what could be a chair's back is picked out by a shaft of sunlight slanting in through broken glass. Behind rigid lines of timber and metal, the hint of curved elegance makes it seem treasure. Howard walks over from the bonfire and glances into the gloom.

"For goodness sake, Sara. This stuff is all junk. That's why it's been left here."

"But what I can see of it from here," Sara says, craning her neck, "looks lovely."

"Listen. Let's just get this done as quickly as possible, shall we? I said when we bought this place I didn't want to spend forever sorting through this rubbish. Even if it *is* a chair, it'll be rotten and full of worm. Let's just get everything out and onto the fire."

Sara says nothing, but resolves not to finish work on the contents of this particular outbuilding until Howard is back at the office. In any case, she thinks, it will take far longer than one morning to clear it all. She looks more closely, trying to assess the task. The chair has largely been buried under odd lengths of timber and garden tools and there's some kind of rusty metal

41

framework she can't identify. Sickly, but tough-looking brambles have forced their way in. They reach through the window and gaps in the roof, binding the debris together. Over it all, dirt and the patina of neglect has settled. She begins to tug at the nearest planks of wood and the rotten edges come to pieces in her hands. She gathers the fragments and takes them to the bonfire. Nathan is determined to help and trails her, his hands full of the decaying crumbs. "Mind you don't get splinters, Nath. Put your gloves on like Damien has."

Returning to the outhouse, Sara pulls out an old hoe and a shovel, its edge eroded with use: Munro's use, for it is his shovel and Clara's hoe. Sara stops and takes off a glove to feel properly the hoe's wooden handle. Dryness and dankness have opened-wide the grain. She runs her fingers along the smoothness and wonders about the hands that wore down the wood: whose hands they were, which summers they worked. She takes the old tools and places them on the fire, watching the flames lick round.

It takes her two days to reach Clara's rocking chair; the first day with Howard and the children at home, the second with just Nathan. As she nears her goal, she begins to slow down. Catching ever-closer glimpses of the chair's pocked brokenness she works on, her face turned to the floor. Her hands at last reach the chair and she drags it out into the sunshine, bumping the rockers across stony ground. Two of the spindles in the chair's back are broken, the pieces missing. Damp has loosened joints and there's a history written in varnish and paint. Pink, bile-green, cream, yellow, black. And Howard was right, there is woodworm. Futile exercise. The thing is clearly past it.

Arrested now, she stands in the yard. Covered in dirt and cobwebs, she stares at the chair, or rather stares past it. Seeing nothing present, she battles against this minor defeat: the hole in the dam through which the sense of a larger futility threatens to burst. Sun shines on her and the child who plays at her feet. A breeze moves down the valley and into the yard, fans the flames of the bonfire, chases the smoke as it rises, ruffles the hair on the heads of mother and child, offers the blond in it up to the sun. Still Sara does not stir. Miles away, miles away, thinking of Luke. Tears begin to brim. Furious, she jams a fist across her eyes, smears the muck and tears down her face. Determined not to let Nathan see her distress, she fights to smother these images of Luke. How dare he come to her, unbidden? How dare he? He does not budge. Motionless, she turns on him, silently yells, *Alright then, as you are here, what would* you *do with the bloody chair? Howard would burn it. What would you do?* No answer comes and she stands, arms wrapped round herself, rocking gently next to the chair.

In the vastness of the skies, a buzzard circles Blundle Hill, sees and dismisses the woman and child: specks in the largeness of the landscape.

*

The first one in the album was taken outside the registry office. Big, bold photograph, clear colours, crisp in the professional, gilded mount; the moment made captive and preserved behind plastic.

She looks slimmer in the photo, Sara reflects, a lot less tired. Howard was right, she has put on weight since she's had the children. She draws the album towards herself, and catches the scent of the bonfire still about her clothes; evidence of her morning's work as she sits now with her cup of coffee in the kitchen at Trethella. A rare treat to sit with a cup of coffee, alone in the house for once; Nathan settling into his mornings at playschool. She must go and pick him up soon, but first she needs this time. She turns the page. Another photo similar to the first. Sara wearing a pale lemon dress and carrying a small bouquet of lemon and white carnations, freesias, lilies. In this photo, Howard is at her side, looking more or less as he looks now. A little more hair then, perhaps, but not much in it. Smart in his dark suit, he smiles, but does not quite look at the camera. It always makes Sara uneasy to see how, in so many of these photographs, Howard never quite looks at the camera.

She pushes the thought to one side and turns to the next photograph. Howard and herself again, filling the frame this time. Their hands are clasped together in front of their bodies, displaying Sara's new gold ring on which Howard focuses. At the edge of the image, the fall of Sara's dress is a little distended by her belly. It always seems so obvious to her, but probably no one noticed much. She thinks back to that first pregnancy, her dreamlike hugging of the secret to herself, how it had made her feel so connected to Howard. Even when he was miles away on business, she felt she embraced his presence, some quickening part of him deep within her. Such contentment it had seemed at the time. She can see it in these photos now. Through all the paraphernalia of a wedding – family, friends, flowers, formal clothes – there is about her face a kind of absorbed reverie. A calm, almost soporific distancing.

It's evident in the photo near the back of the album too, Sara thinks, casually skipping several pages, using this faultless logic to bring her nearer her objective. She sees through her own ploy. Briefly bites her bottom lip. Takes a sip of coffee.

The images change towards the back of the album. No more crisp, official photographs from the professional's camera. These later ones were taken at the reception by Sara's old school friend, Helen, and given with apologies for horizons askew and feet chopped off. They are not good, but Sara has kept them: a memento.

Her sense of urgency increases as she nears her goal. Where is it? She has gone too far through the album and has to turn back a few pages. Her quick hands stumble and the plastic sticks. There it is. There. A page of four photographs. She fixes on the third.

The door of the marquee had been rolled round itself and secured back, letting in the light of that glorious day, softly sidelighting the figures seated at the table. The other photos on this page are disasters of darkness or red eye and Sara marvels at the luck of the amateur photographer, catching by chance this subtle side-light. Three figures are seated behind a table strewn with discarded plates and half-full glasses of champagne. The hands and knees of another figure are evident at the edge of the photo. Who was that? David, perhaps. On the right of the photo there's Dan, a tall man leaning back in his chair, raising his glass in salute and grinning straight at the camera. He has abandoned his jacket and tie in his half-serious chip-on-the-shoulder assertion that these are the riff-raff friends of Sara. The light from the open doorway falls across his raised arm and highlights the glass in his hand, but his face, as he leans back, is in shadow. At the centre of the photo is Sara, also looking at the camera, smiling her self-absorbed smile, her face and shoulders lit as she leans her folded arms gently on the edge of the table. And on her right – Sara shifts the album nearer – on her right and catching most of the light that comes through the doorway is Luke. It is the one photograph she has of him and she feasts on it, gorging on detail as if that might somehow bring him closer.

Really it is very ordinary. A man, sits at a table, eyes downcast, small smile. Sara sees more, of course. Luke avoids the eye of the camera for reasons that are different from those half-formed thoughts she has about Howard's evasion. There is something wistful about the smile, something dispirited about the downcast eyes. He too has removed his jacket and tie, and the leaning of his head to one side exposes the taut line of his neck to the flooding light. Beautiful. Perhaps, most of all, it is the placement of his body that moves her. Echoing her own position, he rests a forearm on the table which brings one shoulder forward, placing his body in a gentle curve about her and she sees clearly now that which she could only miss then; his sense of tender deference.

The thought steals in of Howard, at work, the breadwinner for his family. Howard at work while she drools over the photograph of someone else. Her guilt floods back. And self- contempt. *For God's sake. Pathetic woman.* Her loneliness assuaged she can afford this anger now. Cleansing anger that burns away her guilt. Still, the knock at the door makes her start. She pushes back her chair, slams the album shut and strides to the door. The back door. People here come to the back door, do they? Through the isometric patterning etched on the glass she can see the figure of a man. Whoever is it? They've hardly met anyone here yet. Tradesman probably.

"Yes?" Sara says wrenching the door open.

The man outside widens his eyes in surprise and smiles. "Hello. I'm Nick Franklin. I live at the first cottage down the lane."

"Ah." Sara, somewhat abashed, finds the grace to proffer a hand and smile. "I'm Sara Williams. I'm afraid I thought you'd come to sell something."

Again the raise of an eyebrow, the calm perusal from mild eyes.

"Only you came to the back door."

A brief laugh. "I did, didn't I? No. On the contrary. Apart from coming to say hello, I was rather hoping to buy something."

"I'm sorry?"

He gives a full smile now. "That is – if you don't want it yourself. Which you quite possibly do as you've gone to so much trouble to dig it out."

Slowly Sara catches his meaning. "The rocking chair?"

He nods his approval. "It's a beauty, isn't it? I don't blame you if you don't want to part with it – but if you decide to keep it and you want a hand with the restoration, I'd be really pleased to help." Sara gazes at him. A sinking sensation makes itself felt in the pit of her stomach. "Sorry," he continues, "You could both be antique experts for all I know."

"No. No. Really the chair was past it."

"Oh no. Not past it."

"Yes, really, it was so bashed and there were layers of paint. And all the joints were loose."

"That can all be sorted."

"And it was full of worm."

"Not so much worm. And I know someone who could turn identical spindles in yew to replace the ones that are missing."

The sinking sensation increases and Sara arms herself with annoyance. "You seem to be exceptionally familiar with it."

He raises his hands in mock surrender. "I confess. I saw it from the footpath the other day. I did knock at the door, but there was no one home, so I'm afraid I wandered into the yard and had a look."

"Oh, *did* you?" Sara retorts.

"Yes, sorry. I've been so used to calling on Rob and Jenny. I tended to just wander in and out. I realise it's a habit I shall have to break."

"I'm sorry." Sara says, turning her face away. "I'm afraid you're too late for the rocking chair. And you'll have to excuse me, I really have to pick my son up from school."

But he has followed her gaze to the yard. Disbelief strikes as he sees the smoke rise. He exhales shocked breath. "You haven't put it on the *bonfire?*"

Her mouth tightens, but he is gone. Three strides take him to the corner of the house, six more across the yard to where the remains of the fire still smoulder. He kicks with the toe of his boot. The last charred curve. Red and black ashes.

*

"That's *much* better, Caroline," Howard says soon after arriving at work on Monday morning. "Perhaps you could open some windows? The smell of paint is quite strong as you come in." He places three fresh flowerheads, stark purple Iris, in the vase on his desk. As Caroline crosses to the window, he sees she is watching him and he smiles up at her. "Attention to detail," he says, nodding to the flowers. "Vital."

He walks round the room. "Your boyfriend seems to have done a good job," Howard continues, then peers behind the radiator where he is met with bare plaster. "Oh dear." He raises his eyebrows in her direction. Caroline shuffles. "Well, never mind," he says moving back towards the desk. "Perhaps you'd like to take the packaging off the chairs this morning? I'm sure the people from the planning department will want to sit down when they come this afternoon. They're due at three. And you will remember to meet the architect at the station? His name's John Davies. Train arrives at 2:17, I think. It's in the diary. And, Caroline, I realize it's outside your normal brief, but, at this early stage, before I engage more staff, I'd be grateful if you would run the vacuum cleaner round before you bring the furniture in. You know how it is with new carpets and although the painter's taken care, there are footprints by the door."

"Oh. Yes. Alright."

"Excellent. While you're doing that, I'll take another walk round outside, see if I can visualize exactly what the planners are making *quite* such a fuss about before they arrive. And, Caroline, we'll need coffee. I do want to be able to offer people proper coffee – not instant. If you could organise that a.s.a.p. – certainly before this afternoon – I'd be grateful."

"Yes, Mr Williams."

"And tea. Quality tea. We ought to be able to offer a variety. And, Caroline . . . "

"Yes, Mr Williams?"

". . . I ought not to have to concern myself with these minor details."

"Oh." Caroline looks at her feet, "sorry."

Howard nods. "It's early days. I think that's everything for now."

"Right, Mr Williams. Thank you."

"Thank *you*, Caroline."

Howard watches her leave the room. In her haste to exit she doesn't open the door quite far enough and has to tilt her ample hips round the door post in order to get out. Good grief. She was the best of a bad bunch. He hopes she will find a little more poise and polish soon. He needs someone to charm clients; not be a doormat for them. No matter. Howard had been careful not to specify her final job description. If – when he took on more staff – she ended up being typist-cum-dogsbody, so be it. He'd made no promises and despite the useful experience she'd stated on her CV, she certainly didn't seem like PA material.

Howard flicks on the recessed spotlights which were also installed over the weekend. He thinks they'll be impressive, although the amount of sunlight currently flooding in, reflecting up from the sea to bounce and sparkle across the ceiling makes it difficult to tell for sure.

He looks round at the transformed room. The painter *has* done a reasonable job, in fact. And – importantly – he delivered on time. It can't have been easy. The walls which had been exposed granite must have taken some covering. Howard's first instinct had been to plaster over the lot, but he smothered this idea in deference to target marketing. His clients here would expect to see rough granite work. It was a very different concept from the one he was used to working with – the slick, crisp lines of suburban clubhouses – but then, that was part of the challenge: using his professionalism in a chameleon-like manner to match the demands of the situation while still overlaying Clarendon's and his own classy high standards. He smiles briefly at his own earnestness. But then, he thinks, that's what makes him so good at his job. His attention to detail *is* very exacting. The role of this office space – in the final complex – will, without a doubt, be minimal. But to give it *for now* the level of attention that the whole complex will eventually receive, to use it *for now* as a microcosm in which to try out, assess and represent concepts, set standards, which can then be applied to the project in its entirety is – he knows from experience – a very valid exercise.

Through the window he sees Caroline getting into her car. On her errand for real coffee, no doubt. Her one great advantage, Howard reflects as he watches her briefly check her appearance in the rear-view mirror, her hand darting quickly to rearrange stray hair, is that he couldn't even begin to fancy her. Thank God for that. It makes life so much simpler.

Although it hasn't rained for several weeks, Howard takes the precaution of changing his shoes for the wellington boots he keeps in the cloakroom cupboard. He knows grass seeds stick to his suit otherwise.

He lets himself out and is struck again by the vastness of the sky and the wildness of the landscape that drops in lowering undulations from the buildings, to the cliff edge, to the sea. He adjusts his tie. The rugged character of the place is, of course, one of its major attractions. Overseeing the sculpting of raw countryside into the manicured contours of a golf course is always an important part of his brief, but, he senses, never more so than here. He walks on across the meadows towards the cliff, wondering what unknown devils this particular terrain holds in store for him before he can quite overcome it. Certainly there are a lot of hedges to be taken out. And not just hedges as he ordinarily thinks of them. The Cornish variety are a massive affair of soil and granite and vegetation. In cross-section they measure around two metres at the base narrowing to rather less than a metre at the top. The ones on the land here are about two metres high. And the fields of this old farmland are tiny; the hedges numerous. He'd worked it out. There were about seven miles of hedge that would have to go. And it would have to be done carefully. He'd flown over this area, seen farmland where the hedges had been removed, the scars still clearly visible. That may be tenable for farming; it would never do for a Clarendon golf course. It probably wouldn't take that long, in fact, but finding the right man to do the job was going to be tough. He'd met one or two of the local contractors already. Bunch of cowboys. Might even have to think about bringing someone down to do it. Expensive business though.

He stops and looks back towards the existing buildings. Sod the planners. They had given permission for the course itself, but their demands for low-level buildings were totally contrary to the drawings Clarendon's architect had produced. It would mean literally going back to the drawing-board, a delay he could well do without. Funding had already been obtained for this project and despite the fact that interest rates were currently so favourable, he wanted to see the scheme up and running as soon as possible. He looks at the lie of the land. What are these people from the planning department on about? He really couldn't see that two-storey buildings would make a blind bit of difference – he would simply have to be his convincing best this afternoon.

Although the June day is sunny, a strong breeze is driving onshore. This region always seems to be windy. He remembers his visit a few years ago when Clarendon first thought of expanding into

Cornwall. It was winter. January. He'd walked along the coast path and the vegetation on the entire cliff face and about half a mile in land had been brown, dead: killed by the lashing of winter weather. That sight was the main thing that had made him vote against the area. The scale of that much natural destruction was not to be underestimated. Ultimately, when the buoyant economy had again brought mention of expansion into Cornwall to the fore, Howard had let himself be talked round. The desecrated area he had seen had been north facing. The area now under discussion faced west-south-west. Much more sheltered.

He turns and looks out to sea and the breeze stirs his hair, finds its way inside his jacket, makes the long grasses beat against his wellingtons, rattles the gorse on the hedge-tops. He turns once more and starts to retrace his footsteps back to the office, wishing he could shake off the sense of disquiet. He didn't feel like this, he reflects, at the start of other assignments. It's just cold feet. An attack of nerves before the ball really starts rolling.

He walks on, his step more determined. There's no way this scheme is going to flounder because of some *git* from the planning department. It may be delayed, but it is *not* going to flounder. Get the meeting over with this afternoon. If it doesn't go his way, get a report made to Head Office – or better still go and see them. It wasn't entirely his fault that things had fallen out as they had, but explanations of this sort were always best done in person. Besides he could use the sanity of London for a couple of days, perhaps even go to see Louisa – he owed himself some light relief. Then if – after the submission of new drawings – the planners still weren't prepared to play ball, it would be time to start pulling a few political strings. He'd rather not go grovelling to Gordon, but Howard knew he had the right contacts and favours owing. Time, then, to start drawing on them.

*

Such beautiful sleep. Sara surfaces from it slowly, coming by degrees to an awareness that it is the middle of the night, that her body is evenly warm and stretched out, luxuriously, across the bed. Where's Howard? Still clumsy with wakening, she reaches out to check; before the thought filters through that he's in London. She turns over: the pleasure of clean linen on naked skin and space to expand into.

The room is very dark, only the faint red glow from the clock beside the bed. 3:42. The curtains are open and the window slightly ajar. The night reaches in, damp and mild and bringing with it, on a soft breeze, the low moan from the lighthouse. Fog. She can feel the dampness in the air that stirs about her face. She really ought to get up and close the window, but the fog-horn calls again; a long, sad note that takes time to trail away into nothingness and she finds herself sleepily listening, waiting for the next sounding, which comes, melancholic. Her body is utterly relaxed; her drowsy mind intent only on fixing the point at which the voice of the breeze is left without its sonorous overtone. There? Yes. The sound of air alone now, lazily sighing through sycamore trees outside the window. It does sound like a sighing, this flow of breeze through wet leaves. She listens for the lower note of the fog-horn, but it does not come; only the resonance of a breathing darkness. There *is* a breathing. Her attention draws itself back into the room and she laughs quietly in recognition, reaches a hand out of bed and locates the soft fur of the cat, curled up on the chair. Quiet enough to hear a cat breathe. He begins purring, raucous through the silence of the night; lifts his head to her touch. Sara's lips form themselves into a smile. The cat in the bedroom. Howard would have a fit. She wonders how his time in London is going. He's been so tense lately.

She gets out of bed without turning on the light and begins to rescue her dressing gown from beneath the cat, then leaves it where it is, feeling her way to the bedroom door without it. As she's awake, she'll just go and check on the children.

In darkness she crosses the landing. From the depths of the dark stairwell a tangible calm reaches up to her belly. She stops, gives herself to it, then moves on, guiding herself to the children's bedroom by keeping one hand on the granite wall.

Damien is half out of bed as usual. She takes hold of his arm which is hanging to the floor, crosses it over his chest and lifts him back into the centre of the bed. Her face touches his warm body, picks up the healthful smell of him. She draws the duvet lightly back in place. Now Nathan. Her hands reach out in the darkness and lightly touch his sleeping form. The shoulder, the hip, the duvet clear of his face; he's fine.

Toeing Lego aside with bare feet, she crosses to the window and leans on the frame, nosing out into the darkness. The moisture drifts in, cool on her face and shoulders and breasts. Poised there, she can hear Nathan's even breathing and, outside, the soft stirring of foggy air. She wonders how far the fog reaches. How far the blanket spreads.

The night is warm and close about her as she crosses back to her room. She goes to the window and pauses again, listening to drops of water dripping from fog-drenched leaves and to the plaintive sound of the fog-horn. Such balm: it seems sacrilege to shut it out. But the breeze pushes in and the curtain that drapes itself against her thigh is languid with damp. *Alright, alright.* Yielding to the voice of reason, she slides the casement closed. Tumbling back into bed, she supposes that, as she's been awake, she will lie restless for some time. Three minutes later she is deeply asleep.

*

Heart thumping now, his breath comes in short gasps. Sweat lathers the small of his back. He jerks a foot behind to rid himself of the duvet and she uses his momentary shifting of weight to slither sideways, as if she would squirm from under him. *The bitch.* Sucking air through clenched teeth, he slides his body to recover her – his penis caught between bellies greased with viscous wet. *Christ.* Her legs are clammed, vice-like, to lock him out, yet he feels the thrust of her hips and, pushed to him, the tautness of her nipples. He tips his head back to clear his mouth of her hair and the blood beats in his head. *For fuck's sake, Louisa.* Fingernails claw and he reaches back to their punishing. The wrist he wrenches forward is matchwood in his fist. At this last she gives and he knees her thighs apart, ramming himself hard home. Gaining oblivion with the giving of seed. And release. Oblivion. Release.

Spent, he drops his whole weight on her, lying widthways across the bed. As the pounding of his heart subsides, he hears laughter and raised voices filtering up from the darkened street. The clatter of a beer can, kicked, cuts through the night. He opens his eyes and his vision is filled with red numerals – 3:42 – vivid then pale as the flash of red neon enters the room. Now vivid, now pale. Now vivid, now pale. His steadying breath chimes in with the timing.

*

Nathan screams as the train pulls in and the brunt of noise blasts through him. Sara laughs in the din and scoops him up, hugs his little body against her own to lend it weight. "I said it would be loud," she calls, her lips brushing his ear. He clings to her, turning in her arms to watch the engine as it passes, eyes wide with distrust. "It's alright, it won't leap off the rails. Come on, let's find your Dad."

Two days apart have done them good she thinks, her stride alive as she walks down the platform. In rays of light through the filigree of ironwork, scattered pigeons fly from her feet.

A man gets down from the train wearing Howard's clothes and Howard's face, only much older. He expects to take a taxi and does not look for a welcoming party and Sara sees the unguarded countenance, downcast as he steps from the carriage. He turns away towards the rear of the train and it is left to Sara to follow him along the platform. Wrestling with the shock of his round-shoulderedness, her own gait becomes less certain. She calls his name, but – dreamlike – the sound is lost.

The passengers flow past in the opposite direction and she supposes he must know of some other exit, but he reaches the guard's van and turns in there, allowing her to catch him.

"Are you alright?"

He turns abruptly at the sound of her voice and the frown is replaced by a wry smile and he holds her eye a second before Nathan reaches out to him. "What are you doing here?" he asks quietly.

"We came to meet you. Are you okay?"

The doors of the guard's van rattle and are opened from within. He looks away. "Yes. Fine. I've been asleep on the train. Had a whisky soon after Plymouth and slept the rest of the way. Not ideal, in fact - I had some papers to go through."

"How did it go?"

"Okay. Good to be back in civilization."

Nathan reaches out again and Sara must either put him down or pass him to Howard. Howard chucks him briefly under the chin. "Not now, Nathan. Look, I've brought something for your mother." The guard is clattering parcels to the edge of the carriage. "Eh. Gently with that, thank you," Howard calls to him as he brings his purchase from the back of the van. A rocking chair, bound for the journey in corrugated card.

"Howard!"

"I know how sorry you were about the other one."

Sara blushes. Her folly in burning a restorable antique is

something she has kept to herself. After all, Howard had said burn it. To confess her own guilt would have been to implicate him also. By sparing herself she spared him. Yet she blushes and her pulse rate quickens. Howard picks up the chair, places it down gently out of harm's way.

"You weren't supposed to see this until it was home and unpackaged. Which car did you come in?"

"Yours."

"We should be able to fit it in then."

"Yes, if we leave the boot open. Howard, it's so kind of you to think of this." She is genuinely moved. Certainly it will be a pleasure to have a rocking chair in the house, but it is the fact that he has found time to think of her that is really touching. She reaches out, softly catches his arm and smiles, head on one side. "Thank you," she says, holding his eye.

He smiles briefly. "Don't be daft. Let's go shall we?"

"Of course. I'm sorry. You're tired."

He did take a taxi after all. Sara had to pick Damien up from school and Howard was anxious to get out to the office to see how things had gone in his absence. He was expecting a delivery of seed.

Ballerina

Sam Goodall

Sam Goodall: happy to be here since 1972. Courtesy of his Mum, Dad and Margaret.

A slight white figure whirls around on the stage far below John's gaze. Effortlessly bounding and spinning Estella Rostand glides in and out of John's transfixed stare. His head follows her every move from left to right, up and down the stage. Her tiny frame ghosts across the lenses of his glasses, trapped in the border of thick black plastic like a star on a screen; her flickering white light escaping and returning each time she moves to the part of the stage that John cannot afford to see. No matter how far he leans forward, craning from his dark corner in the heights of the theatre she always disappears. He is lost in the dark, in the cheap seats, only visible by the reflection in his spectacles. If someone had been looking at him even staring at him, he would not have seen them. His eyes only see the little white flame dancing far below.

At the end she takes her bow, and John stands up, and cheers and claps until his throat is sore and his hands burn. He cannot even see her as she bows to the floor, arms laden with flowers. Again she is on the expensive part of the stage. But John doesn't mind. He cheers and claps until the final murmur of applause is lost beneath the rustling of chiffon and silk, and the audience begins to move.

John shuffles out into the half-lit night at the front of the theatre. The air is thick with the sound and smell of burbling taxi engines. Large women in yards of shining green and crimson are looking about for the evening suits with which they came. Monuments of hair and flashing baubles crowd around as John shuffles out of the light and into the cold. He pulls his Army Surplus coat around him and plods up the street away from the glowing throng. When John started going to the ballet, he felt very self-conscious about his scruffiness, but now he doesn't think about it; he hardly even notices that anybody else is there. When he reaches the top of the hill that leads away from the theatre he turns and looks back. In his glasses: the tiny reflection of the large stone building, classical pillars rising up into the dark night, framing the people and light that swarm like a distant fire.

John gets off the bus and walks the final quarter-mile back to his flat. The familiar smell of piss that he has never quite got used to welcomes him as he opens the door into the stairway. It is almost pitch black inside except for the glow from the third-floor light, the only one that isn't broken. John trudges up the seven flights to his top-floor flat, splashing blindly through the puddles of water that have accumulated in the stairwells. On the sixth flight he feels in his pocket for his keys, groping with his fingers to find the Yale. Then he feels for the place where he knows the door handle will be and prods into the dark with the key until it finally finds the hole.

A bare electric bulb lights up his tiny hallway. In the mirror by the telephone, he turns to see his face, thin and bony, the pale skin stretching as if there is not quite enough to cross the hollows of his cheeks. From behind his glasses stare two large watery blue-grey eyes. He pushes back a mat of hair that has fallen across his forehead, stares at himself for a few more seconds and turns away. He throws his coat onto the armchair in the corner of his living room, and walks into the kitchen. He stands and watches his baked beans in the pan as they slowly come to the boil. Stirring them vigorously he stews them down into the baby slop he prefers as they belch and puff with steam in resistance. Through the kitchen door he is able to look through into the living room and see himself stirring his pan. There is a long dressing mirror leaning against the wall opposite. It is about a foot wide and six feet tall. John watches himself out of the corner of his eye, shoulders and back arching over the saucepan, hair falling down in soft brown strands across his face; his hand automatically directing the wooden spoon in a figure of eight through the orange mush. He closes his eyes and the little white dancer on the stage begins to whirl around his mind in a double loop. But each time she is about to close the figure, she disappears. John opens his eyes again. In the mirror he sees puffs of grey cloud emerging from underneath his saucepan. He yanks the grill pan out with his free hand whilst the other carries on its subconscious course with the spoon. Two slices of toast smoulder in front of him on the greasy wires of the grill.

He spoons a final forkful of beans into his mouth, and puts his knife and fork side by side on the plate with the half-eaten remains of one of the slices of toast. He takes a sip from a mug of tea, sits back in his chair and stares at the wall. Staring hard at the flaking grey paint in front of him he leans forward and peels back a scale of it. There is a round white patch forming where he has done this many times before. It feels for him like picking at a scab in reverse. He can just reach forward and peel it back flake by flake. John's chair does not face into the middle of the room, it faces the wall in the corner adjacent to the kitchen door with just enough space for him to sit down with his toes touching the skirting board. John can watch himself eating his tea in the mirror and he can watch himself picking at the paint on the wall. There is no other furniture in the room, just a cassette recorder in one corner and a print of a Degas' *Ballerina* next to the mirror.

John scrapes the remains of his tea into the dustbin. The soggy bread slides off the plate like a slug, onto the back of a bread bag that is covered in sooty scrapings from the toast. John goes back into the living room and begins to undress. Pulling off his heavy jumper, slowly removing all his clothes he carefully folds them onto his chair, until he is standing just in a pair of greying boxer shorts and a khaki T-shirt that is beginning to split across the shoulders. Facing the kitchen he stands upright and rolls his shoulders up and down and gently rotates his ankles. Then he spreads his legs about two feet apart and his head falls forward from his shoulders, down between his thighs. He stares at himself in the mirror, his long white face hanging inverted in the angle of his legs; all framed by black whorls of hair on the backs of his thighs. He drops his arms down from by his sides, turns his face downward, and stretches out his hands for the floor, the tips of his fingers just touching the red, black and orange twists of the old paisley carpet. He gently begins to bounce up and down, alternately stretching left and right, down toward his feet. The strain of his tendons just making his face twist as he bites down gently on the edge of his lip.

Then he starts to stretch more vigorously left to right, from toe to toe. Each time feeling the strain of his muscles and ligaments as he pulls and stretches for a little more give. Touching his toes, then his calves, then straightening, stretching for the ceiling and again to the left and then the right. Then he lies on the floor, lifting his legs up and down in short sweeps. He stretches himself in every direction from every angle, like a child with a piece of blu-tack. He lifts his leg onto the back of the armchair and stares at himself, leaning down as near to his knee as he can reach, then straightening and sweeping his arm up and down like a languid streamer in a breeze. Then he drops his leg off the chair and repeats the same in reverse. Finally he leaves the chair and skips over to his tape recorder, leaping and wiggling his feet, stretching out his arms to meet in an oval as he goes. Standing over the tape player with his feet at right angles to each other from the heel, he slowly leans down, without bending his knees, lowering an arm in a graceful arc toward the play button. Just giving a little curtsy at the very last moment so that he can reach.

The servos and capstans of the tape recorder let out a gentle hum and a hiss through the speakers as the slack is taken up and the feeder tape winds through. Finally, a distant violin begins to cover the hiss of the machinery. John straightens himself slowly as the music begins to grow and fill the room. Then almost imperceptibly he moves just stretching out a leg, then shifts his weight onto it and stretching out the other. As the music quickens so does John until he is making a small circuit of the room in staccato leaps, with as much grace as he can muster. All the time watching himself in the mirror, apart from in one place in the room, opposite the chair, where he just cannot see. Then, very suddenly the music stops and so does John, poised like a statue on one leg.

And as suddenly as it stopped it starts again only this time much faster. Leaping forward, he starts to whirl round the room like Estella Rostand, a tiny figure of eight across the paisley carpet, leaping and stretching and spinning. Round and around, the music filling his ears, pushing him on, around and around and around. Spinning and spinning until his head is dizzy like a drunk. The armchair, the scab, the kitchen door, the mirror and the ballerina passing repeatedly before his eyes. The lights outside the window and in the kitchen blurring and skidding as if he is a child on a fairground ride. And finally he falls, stumbling into a heap on the floor, panting and puffing. The music still thrumming through his head as the room slowly returns to a standstill. Sweat covers his face, flushed crimson from the neck upwards, his chest heaving as the music finally dies and the tape player snaps to a halt.

In the silence of the dimly lit room he just lies there, his breathing slowly returning to normal. Watching himself in the mirror, until the whiteness has returned to his face. Slowly he picks himself off the floor, puts his glasses back on and walks into his bedroom.

A harsh beeping wakes him at 7:30 a.m. The red digits of the clock scream at him from the far side of the room to get up. He pulls back the duvet and swings himself out of bed. His hand lands with a thump on the little white box, swatting it into silence. John hates having to get up so early. If it were not for Estella he would stay in bed all day. From his window he sees the low winter sun losing its battle with the dirty grey clouds and fog that hang over the city. By the time John has dressed and is outside, the monochrome greyness has entirely closed over. John retraces his steps of the night before, a couple of streetlights just flickering off as he walks to the bus stop. The grey theatre is almost lost in the cold grey haze as he walks back down the hill.

Inside the ticket office there are three short queues. Mostly young people, students and a couple of travellers with backpacks. John resents their presence. He is desperate to get to the front. He keeps hearing the ticket women saying, "there are only a few seats left" and, "I'm afraid you won't be able to sit together."

John wants to say, "I'll take them. I don't mind – I want to sit alone."

But he can't. The couple in front of him look at each other and speak softly in French or something. Eventually, they nod to the lady and take the tickets. John's neck begins to glow slightly pink and he bites his teeth together in anger. They had taken ages to decide and John could see the queues beside him moving more quickly; taking the last of the tickets.

"Have you got any standbys left, please?"

"We've only got seats in the circle love, nothing in the gallery, sorry. Haven't you seen it enough times now?"

John ignores her and stares at the counter so as not to be in her gaze.

"How much is the circle?"

"Twenty-three pounds love, all the cheap seats have gone today I'm afraid."

John feels in his pockets for what remains of his Giro. He knows that he doesn't have enough but he pulls out the money and looks at it anyway, two crumpled fivers and some loose change. He only just had enough for a twelve pound standby at the back of the gallery. He holds it out in his palm between him and the ticket lady and stares at it, hoping somehow that he hasn't seen a tenner beneath the change or that maybe the ticket woman will take pity on him and let him have the seat anyway.

"Maybe tomorrow, eh love?"

John looks up at her for the first time. She is smiling at him. John manages to just raise the edges of his mouth in response but he is still biting down on his teeth in bitter resignation; the tiny muscles around the curve of his jaw trembling with the force of his disappointment. He feels like he did as a child when he knew that he was about to cry. He turns away and leaves the ticket office and walks the four miles back to his flat. The cold air stings at his eyes whenever he raises his head from the hunched slouch of his walk.

Back at his flat he walks straight into his bedroom, and pulls off his clothes down to his T-shirt and shorts, and climbs back under his duvet. When he wakes he looks out of the window to see the the last thin edge of a molten pink sun slipping beneath the trees on the horizon to the west of the city. Someone once told him the sun only sets pink because of all the shit in the atmosphere. John was half sorry to see the sun had beaten back through the greyness. He thought grey was a more honest colour.

Without the ballet, John just sits all night staring at the the scab on the wall. He reads a little but mostly he stares either at himself or at the scab. Finally he decides that he should eat. And then, as the night before, he undresses and begins his stretches, but tonight he just stretches. Hour after hour, bending and twisting himself in every possible direction. He does not dance, he just stretches and stretches every muscle and tendon in his body. When he hears the sounds of a bird tweeting outside his window he finally stops. This is the sound that makes him feel most unhappy and alone. It is still dark outside but somewhere there is a bird singing. John knows that the greyness of dawn is only a few minutes away. So he stops stretching and goes into his bedroom, shuts the thin yellow flower print curtains and crawls under his duvet. John has always hated those curtains as the cold grey of the morning starts to seep through the yellow flowers and leaves. He hates the curtains so much that he once tried to move his bed so that he could not see them. But the room was too narrow and the bed would only fit one way. So now he sleeps with his head at the other end of the bed; the curtains hanging above him and the grey vapour of dawn creeping over him. But at least he cannot see the twisted faces that had stared out from the shadows of every yellow flower and green leaf. Eventually he sleeps.

John doesn't get up that morning. It is a Friday and there are never any standbys at the weekends. So he stays in bed, huddled beneath the duvet until the sun is once again dipping low beneath the horizon; but when John gets up he starts his exercises straight away, stretching and bobbing until he can hardly move. Then again he cooks his tea and picks at the scab until he feels he can stretch some more. He doesn't dance. He stops dancing altogether. He just stretches. He stops getting up as well. Estella Rostand has finished her run at the theatre and is not set to return for several months; but he keeps stretching. Soon he is able to get both legs behind his neck, touch his knees with his head and can almost do the splits. He hardly leaves the house at all now that Estella has gone, except to cash his giro and to buy the bread and the tins he needs for food. Eventually John's stretching also stops. Not because he has lost interest but because he can stretch himself no more. He is like a rubber band. He can roll up into the tiniest ball, raise his leg so it is parallel to his torso; he can do anything. He still slouches back and forth to the post office and the supermarket, but underneath he knows that at any time he can leap forward like a gazelle, bounding and stretching out like his ballerina. So he stretches just enough every day to maintain his flexibility and he even starts getting up in the morning, and he hardly notices that the sun still sets pink.

Then one day in the Job Centre when he is standing in the queue to sign on, John notices a job on one of the noticeboards.

> *Wanted, part-time caretaker for city theatre. No experience required. £2.75 p.h.*

To his surprise he picks the card off the noticeboard and takes it to the Job Enquiries desk.

"Customers are requested not to remove the cards from the noticeboards, please Sir."

"Oh, sorry. I was just wondering whether it was still available."

"Well, it wouldn't be on the noticeboard if it weren't still available now would it Sir?"

"No I guess not – look I thought you were here to help us not take the piss." John hardly recognises the fluidity of his unbroken speaking voice. It is as if the bendy man beneath his khaki T-shirt and shorts has spoken.

"Er, yes sir, sorry Sir, it's been a long day – now what's the reference number?"

John can hardly believe it as the white shirt makes a special effort to get him an interview before the weekend. John can believe it even less as he walks out of the theatre with the words "You can start on Monday," ringing in his ears. The bendy man had done the talking then as well.

"Once swept the stage at the Royal Opera House."

How could they believe that? But they did, and for the first time in his life he has a job.

So John sweeps the stage and cleans out the dressing rooms, always in the back of his mind doing it for Estella Rostand. He is always tidying up for her return. And he keeps on bending and he keeps on stretching, but not quite as much now that he has a job. He even buys himself a TV with some of the money from work. And eventually the posters that he has been waiting for go up.

Estella Rostand returns to her highly acclaimed role as . . .

Finally the day comes that Estella begins rehearsals. The first time he sees her she is standing at the front of the stage, stretching. A tiny figure in tatty tights and leg warmers, stretching out her toes as the director spins clumsily about the stage before her.

"Extend, Esty darling, extend - do you see, do you see?"

John doesn't see, he just leans on his broom and watches Estella; he has never seen her so close, he has never even seen her on that part of the stage before. Estella doesn't see either, but she does see John. As she lifts her head from her knee she smiles, straight at him, into his eyes. And he looks away, feeling a flush rise in his cheeks as he looks down at the ground and sweeps the floor around his feet. He thought that she could not see him standing in the dark wings at the back of the stage. So he moves back a little further into the shadows.

Everyday he sweeps the wings when she is rehearsing, and then he sweeps the theatre boxes, where he can sit and watch as if they were sharing a private audience. Then one day John is watching her from the Royal Box. As she skims across the stage in effortless leaps she stumbles, and as she falls there is an audible click and she crashes onto the stage. John jumps up from his seat and sees Estella's face twist with pain as she grasps at her ankle as the director rushes over to her.

"Oh my goodness, Estella – don't move, don't move. I'll get help."

He begins to shout for help as he holds Estella's ankle, and she presses her head against his arm. As he looks around the theatre for help, he sees John and a scowl forms across his face. He spits out his call for help once more.

"Don't just stand there man, help for God's sake, help."

John rushes down the backstairs, his face burning with shame and uncertainty at what he will find on the stage. There is still nobody else on the stage as he runs over and kneels beside Estella. At first he does not look at her face, he just looks hard at the director for instruction.

"Take her arm man, take her arm."

John reaches for her arm and sees her face red with pain and a few tears just beginning to slip down her cheeks. The first touch of his hand on her arms is almost too much for him, his fingers pressing softly onto her warm skin, just withdrawing momentarily as if they have touched something unreal. They lift her between them and it is like lifting air, her weight almost nothing as she is cradled off the stage with her arms around their shoulders.

In Estella's dressing room they lift her onto a bench and and she falls back into the pillow and sighs. She has stopped crying and John passes her a tissue from her dressing table. As she takes the tissue she looks at him for the first time and the look of distress on her face turns to a smile.

"*Merci, merci beaucoup*," she says. She sits up and kisses John on both cheeks, and then before John knows it, he is being ushered out by the director.

"Make room for the doctor lad. Go on, you can get back to your sweeping now."

So John goes back to his sweeping.

The next day when John sweeps the stage he only sees the director and he asks if Estella is alright. He says that she is fine, just a slight sprain and she will be alright in a couple of days. So when she returns John watches her dance from out of the shadows. She smiles at him when he catches her eye, and she says hello whenever she sees him; sweeping the stage wings, sweeping the floor around his feet.

As the first night approaches John can hardly remember ever being happier. When he gets paid that week he goes straight to the ticket office and buys himself a ticket for the opening night. He gets a seat in the middle of the dress circle, the most expensive seat in the house. Even with a staff discount it is ninety-three pounds. But not only does John buy the most expensive ticket he also gets himself an evening suit and on the night of the performance he buys a bunch of flowers to give to Miss Rostand, and he gets a taxi to the theatre.

From the moment that Estella steps onto the stage John is mesmerized. She spins about the stage, her flickering light again trapped in the lenses of his spectacles, but this time the stage is all his and she cannot escape his gaze. With her every move John feels the stretching of his tendons as she bends and twists across the floor. John feels every sinew that she moves, move in him. And at the interval he just closes his eyes and dances every move over again in his mind. But this time he is her shadow. Every move they make is perfectly in unison, every step applauded, every leap and turn cheered. And then she returns and John is again lost in the darkness. Her flickering light burning brighter and brighter like a flame sucking more and more oxygen; burning onto his mind, radiating out like a star. When it is over he cheers and claps, then sits back in his ninety-three pound seat until he has the theatre to himself. He just sits with his eyes closed, the applause for Estella ringing in his ears.

"Oi John, is that you? Can't keep away from the place can yer? Come on son, get off home. We want to pack the place up and go."

Mr Neville, the head caretaker, is standing with his hands in his pockets at the back of the theatre.

"Yes of course Mr Neville, goodnight."

"Goodnight John, see you in the morning."

John gets up and leaves. He realizes he still has the flowers that he had meant to throw onto the stage.

Outside the theatre there is still a lot of chiffon and hair, and John stands for a moment wondering whether he should get a taxi or take the bus. As a he waits, a side door of the theatre opens and a tiny woman in tracksuit bottoms and a puffy jacket steps out. John does not immediately see that it is Estella. Her hair is not tied back in the usual tight bun, but is falling across her face in thick waves. As she approaches, John raises the bunch of flowers that he is holding, and looks straight at her and smiles.

"Bonjour Miss Rostand."

But his voice trails off at the end as Miss Rostand bustles straight past him and into a waiting taxi. All that she sees are the dresses, baubles and evening suits that John had seen. John stands for a moment watching the taxi as it drives into the dark. He stands in front of the theatre, until the crowd has cleared and he is the only one left. The flowers that he is holding slip out of his hand and scatter on the pavement and he turns away, back up the hill.

Back at his flat John slumps into his chair, and sits silently in the dark. Eventually he stands and begins slowly to undress. Carefully he folds his suit onto the chair in the corner. He stands in front of the mirror, he is wearing a new 'exercise grey' T-shirt and white boxer shorts, finally he removes these as well. He leans down, touches his toes and begins to stretch. Left, right, up, down, left, right, up, down . . .

And as he stretches, he closes his eyes. Then he sits down and spreads his legs, bending his head down to his knees, *left right, left right, left right*, and then to the middle. His face against the carpet between his knees, his back bent double. Then he raises his knees until he is bizarrely hunched over himself. He opens his eyes and his limp penis is curled in a tangle of pubic hair no more than six inches from his face. Then with his hand he begins to caress the forlorn prick and it starts to swell.

John feels his back begin to strain as he arches forward. Every muscle in his back seeming to resist as he presses his head down. The bones in his neck and spine begin to scream as if they are about to shatter, every millimetre that he cranes forward wrenching his contorted spine; all the time his hand caressing more life into his swelling cock. His head moves down and his back gives and gives, millimetre by millimetre he realizes that he is able to touch himself and he closes his eyes and lunges between his legs. There is a dreadful cracking as if a hundred knuckles have been clicked and John takes the shining, taut prick into his mouth.

In the darkness there is a tiny white light flickering around in a circle. John can feel almost nothing as his head gently moves against the sharp resistance of his spine. If he could have seen the mirror he would only have seen his hair fallen around his head as it gently bobbed; the only movement of his acutely contorted body.

A trickle of come oozes onto his tongue and he lets out a

pathetic sigh and a sickening gulp, his head springing back against the doubled-up tension in his bones, he falls back against the floor. A dribble of saliva and wank slides down his cheek and he lies motionless. A tiny heaving of his chest the only sign of life. He lies unmoving in the darkness until the saliva has dried in a smear across his face.

Then very slowly John raises his head and the rest of his body until he is standing bolt upright. He steps over to his tape recorder, bends straight down with a tiny flourish of his arm and presses the play button. As before, the capstans and servos hiss and he begins to dance. Around and around he whirls as the music begins to speed up and everything in the room turns to a blur. Once more he spins and he leaps: the shadow of Estella. Reeling, stumbling and falling about the room as he tries to shut his eyes and bring back her light. Each time he falls he leaps straight up again and carries on spinning and jumping and spinning and leaping. And when the tape stops he turns it over, and carries on until he can hardly move, every muscle in his body burning. His skin scuffed bloody-red and grazed where he has burnt himself from the falls onto the carpet. His stomach is twisted and knotted, his head and vision soupy with images of the spinning room until finally he crashes heavily to the floor, violently retching pale green bile onto the floor. A tendril of the phlegmy bile quivers from the side of his mouth as he crouches doubled over on his knees in agony; repeatedly retching, his stomach and throat burning, as they try to empty themselves of nothing.

And as the greyness of dawn begins to seep through John's bedroom curtains he is still crouched on the carpet by a shiny puddle where his vomit has seeped into the paisley pattern. The round scab of white above the chair is shining like a pale sun in the deathly morning light as John slowly picks himself up and goes into his bedroom. He crawls under his dirty coverless duvet. He does not get up for work that morning or any morning. He does not even see the sun set pink through the shit. He just lies there huddled under the duvet, waiting for the light to go away.

Extract From

Sybil's Jar

Briarly Kate Hardage

Briarly Kate Hardage was born in Los Angeles, California in 1971. She is currently working on a novel provisionally titled *Sybil's Jar*. This piece is an excerpt from the first section.

My Aunt Theo once told me it was entirely possible that the exact replica of everyone on Earth existed, right next to us and side by side, only not in carbon-based life forms. We could be doing anything, just going about our business, and they'd be there with us copying our movements. We weren't alone that way, not truly. Even though we felt like it sometimes, we could never be sure. Just because you can't see someone doesn't mean they aren't there.

She said this to me when I was ten, rocking away in the close summer night on her front porch. She was eating sunflower seeds, cracking the hard salty shells with her teeth and then spitting them into a cracked terracotta flowerpot next to her feet, while I pushed the swing back and forth with one foot: higher, slower, never jarring the rhythm enough to break her stride.

She told me a lot of things like that; she lived alone in a big old house in Kansas near a town called Finley, which no one from anywhere farther away than thirty miles has ever heard of. She lived surrounded by books and cats, and had quite a few theories about the world that she had picked up from the smatterings of science, primarily astronomy, that she liked to read.

My whole family was like that: my father was a professor of Gothic fiction, and spent most of his time holed up in his rooms at the University, researching the parallels between writers' lives and their works. He was obsessed with the Bronte's, which is why we nearly got their names: Emily and Charlotte. When we were born he said that the only thing he needed was another set of twins so he could have an Anne and a Branwell. Aunt Theo said that he had strange ideas, and that children's names held karmic significance. It was a grave mistake to saddle us with such heavy weights so young. He said that they wrote novels and what did she know about it. Theo sighed and said time would tell. So we were Sybil and Sylvia instead: names whose karma was never good either.

I used to spend a lot of time at Aunt Theo's; summers mostly, and whenever my parents needed to be alone, which was quite a bit. My father referred to these stretches of time as 'mother's quiet time,' when what he meant was that neither of them could stand to look at me any more. It was because of Sylvia. Of course, most things were; even Aunt Theo's story about the aliens and her belief in reincarnation, which was based on the theory that we are perpetually surrounded by those we once loved in a sort of cosmic web. When she told me that one I was nine, and I imagined a web like Spiderman's hand, rays of silk shooting out of his palm, which I also confused with the stigmata. For years I looked at my palm, tracing the lines rising, diverging, intersecting, fading away into the cracks in my hand, and tried to picture a web rising up, connecting me to her. I knew that a spider could feel any vibrations on its web, could feel it disconnecting when it snagged, or something ripped through it. I thought that Sylvia must be alive because otherwise I would feel it too, would sense a snap in the thread connecting us. I thought if I was very careful I could make sure.

I didn't tell anyone this, it was just something I did, like so many things. Stepping on cracks ten at a time, right in the middle, waiting two and a half rings before I picked up the phone, keeping the fourteen-carat mark facing up on the ring that my father gave me the year it happened. I lived by ritual, and in silence, convinced that I was achieving something, or at least holding something at bay. Or inviting it in.

When Aunt Theo died, she left her house, her books, her few remaining cats and her wood-sided station wagon to me. So I moved back. I had nothing better to do. In a way I didn't want to come back. I had grown used to the big city: New York, where I lived in welcome obscurity in a run-down apartment next door to Jack Smith. Jack was just like his name, he was everything an average guy should be. We had been kids together, just us running around playing tennis against the cracked backboard at the park, hours in the hot summer sun listening to the hollow thwop of the ball landing above the line. Then walking back home and hoping that the old guy who drove the ice-cream bicycle would be there, like the gatekeeper at the end of the street. We ate Sno-Cones: small paper flutes of crushed ice with some sort of blue and red syrup poured all over. They were the cheapest things he sold, you could get two for fifty cents. Whenever I smell the clay of an old tennis court, or if there is a certain colour to the light: slate blue, almost pink at the horizon, I see Jack: racquet swinging at low-hanging leaves drooped over a cooling sidewalk, his mouth a grotesque purple, melting ice trickling down his arm. Sticky syrup and rising sap; and even now it is almost unbearably painful.

On paper, and when I explained it to my friends back East, it all seemed so idyllic. People picture the Midwest a certain way because they need to; they want an old-fashioned, soda fountain life to exist somewhere so that they can feel smug that they don't have to live in it. In a way I guess it was like that. The cold of the marble-topped soda fountain, my legs sticking to the red plastic seats, cracked open and badly taped over, some yellow stuffing still oozing out. I can remember all this like it was, because everything that I did was always in brilliant technicolour, every activity sorted and filed in my mind, so that when Sylvia came back she would be able to catch up easily. I didn't want her to feel left out of anything, the way you did when you went away for the summer and came back to hear about all the sleepovers you missed.

When I went away to school I worried that it would be too big a jump for her, that it would take too long to explain everything. I guess that by then I suspected for real that she wouldn't be coming back. It took that long. Growing up, I refused to have the other twin bed taken out of my room, but I wouldn't let friends sleep on it. I made them bring sleeping-bags. I thought, I don't know, nothing was ever logical about it, I thought she might climb back in the window one night: swing over from the branch of the old elm tree that overhung our room, catapult into bed. *You'll never guess where I've been.* I thought that I wouldn't tell my parents, I'd just let them see when they came in to check on me. They did that at least five times a night. I'd see the crack of light from the hall widening, hear soft footsteps, feel breath on my face. I woke up every time. The night Sylvia disappeared my mother sat up all night flicking the porch lights on and off, the way she would do when dinner was on the table.

I didn't tell anyone at school I was a twin: it was too important. I got involved, went home rarely, spent a lot of nights walking around the city.

The first week I bought a map and blocked off all the areas I would need to cover, figuring out that I would have to go everywhere twice, night and day, in case I missed her. I picked a big city because I thought there would be more chance she would be there. A cop once told me that to find someone who was lost for a long time, you had to find the kidnapper in yourself and try to walk in their shoes. I think that had a weird effect on me; it made everyone's motives suspect, everyone's lives fragile. It was a game I would play: how could I take someone away so they couldn't be found, where would I go, how would I keep them. It made it hard to relate to friends. I was too busy identifying their weak spots.

She wasn't there, or anyway her body wasn't. I would sometimes look in the mirror late at night, wondering if we still looked the same. We were identical, but Sylvia had a birthmark shaped like Texas on her hip, right below the curve of her waist. Or where her waist would have curved, like mine. I wondered if she had gotten fat, grown cellulite and saggy arms, moaned about her butt and thighs somewhere. If she was rail-thin, counting each vertebra in bed at night looking at a square of sky out a window. If her hair was still red, was it long or short. If I took someone away the first thing I would do is cut off all their hair and dye it. I'd wait till they were asleep and dye it then, so when they woke up they wouldn't know who they were.

I went through a platinum blonde phase, when I first started working for Envogue. All the women in the office were like that, the kind of forties hairdos that take an hour each morning and involve burning their scalps with peroxide every three weeks to avoid roots. I went into a chic hairdressers', the kind with cappuccino holders on the armrests and videos of models they'd styled on huge televisions everywhere around the place. There was even one mounted on the ceiling over my head when I was being shampooed. The shampoo girl, named Marjoree, she spelled it out when she said it, pronounced with a long 'ay' at the end, pointed out the ones she'd worked on.

"Now her, she's part black. Bleaches her skin you know, like Michael Jackson? She told me herself. Personally, I think it's kinda spooky. Why not be the way you are?"

She swivelled my head around, lathering and rinsing. She had blue streaks in her hair and six earrings in her left ear. When she whispered all her secrets her breath smelled like strawberries. "You know, colouring your hair can really be a major life change. Now you, for example, I don't know I'd probably kill for your red hair, but a blonde, wow. You could really be a Madonna type. You know, lots of eyeliner, get one of those bustier things. Knock 'em dead." She pronounced bustier with a hard "r" at the end, and that's what gave her away.

"Where're you from?"

She looked back at me, bland, neatly boxing her answer. "Missouri originally, but I've been here for five years. Do you know where Missouri is?" She tilted my head right back, spraying a fine mist of warm droplets on my forehead. I nodded, closed my eyes, let the matter drop. It's true, no one in a big city is ever really from there, but very few are from anywhere else either. We all gravitate from the Midwest to either coast, like magnets. Or lemmings. New York and Los Angeles are full of beautiful girls with vacant eyes disclaiming their roots.

My hair turned out well, a pure hard platinum with marcelled waves. I had to have thirteen inches cut off to get the style, but Marjoree was right. I didn't look like myself. I didn't look like Madonna either though, more like one of the Victory Wives in faded print housedresses with Hollywood hair. I was proud of my look, but the people at Envogue said I should smarten up the rest of me to go along with my new career in cosmetics. I was a lipstick namer. Well, I named other things too, like blush and some eyeshadows at a pinch, but mostly I concentrated on lipsticks. Eleanor and SayRee were really in charge of everything else.

Envogue was one of those environmentally friendly cosmetic companies that sprung up in the early nineties. The name was supposed to be a pun: Mr Eliot, our boss explained it all for me my first morning as he was showing me around his domain. "It's a combination, you see? Like 'Env' for our environmental awareness, but 'vogue' for our product. I thought of it myself."

He said this with modest pride, the kind doctors use when they talk about how bad their handwriting is. He was a small, trust-funded man, who had the money to back up those fruity ideas other people come up with when they can't sleep. In addition to Envogue, he also funded a laboratory for the, I believe, sole purpose of genetically engineering a combined lemon-lime that you could eat like an orange. He was an eccentric, though likeable man. And he paid well.

Envogue was a strange place: all the women who worked in my department were from the Midwest, like me. Mr Eliot thought that we had a more compassionate outlook on life than New Yorkers, and he liked the idea of being an urban father-figure to his naive flock. Most of us didn't care anything about the environment, and very few even used the cosmetics. Mr Eliot didn't seem to mind much about that. What he loved to do was start these small companies, wait till they found their niche in the market, then incorporate them into a much larger corporation. He dreamed of one day having his own building, a steel and glass tribute to his ideas. Very few of his brainchildren would ever make it that far, but Envogue was doing all right. A few of the supermodels had mentioned wearing our lipsticks in an MTV segment about fashion and the environment, and all of a sudden sales skyrocketed.

I spent my days staring at smears of lipsticks, trying to come up with names that alliterated, like Sahara Sunset and Amazonian Amber. In the early days I suggested Compost Coral to SayRee, but she didn't think it was funny.

"Really, Syb," she said with her nose wrinkling up the way it did when she was being mock-stern, finger wagging under my nose, "this is no laughing matter. We have to get our message across." She was wearing leather shoes and a Moschino belt.

I worked for them for two years, until Aunt Theo died. Then I came back. I arranged to work from Kansas, on a fancy computer I installed in Theo's old library. They'd send me the colours over the computer, then I'd print them out and come up with names. They were really excited about me going back to the Midwest. They thought that I'd be able to get a whole new slant on things. Mr Eliot even came up with a new line called Prairie Portraits. I didn't think it was a very good name, but he said we could work on it as time passed.

"Just go for it, kid," he said, "feel inspired by all those tumbleweeds and stuff."

I sighed. Next thing he'd be telling me to say hi to Wyatt Earp. But he meant well. They all did; they gave me a going-away party where Eleanor got really drunk on the punch I'd spiked, and spent the afternoon crying in one of the toilet stalls, comforted by SayRee who was squatting on the floor in front of the door trying to talk her out, kind of the way you'd do with a dog you were trying to train.

"Christ my knees," she muttered the next day as I was packing a box with all my things. She showed them to me: they were black and blue where she'd finally knelt down and held Eleanor's hand under the stall door. Eleanor was embarrassed; she was wearing sunglasses and black leather, trying to disguise her feelings with the biker-chick look. I would miss them. It's not every company that would keep me on, and I felt bad for Mr Eliot, who I'd always said was such a fruitcake. He was, it was true, but he was also generous. He'd even paid for half of my moving expenses, muttering something about employee relocation costs.

I drove cross-country in a U-Haul, mailing them all postcards from the little towns I passed through. I even sent Eleanor a pecan log from a roadside diner chain called Stuckey's, which was famous for this particular delicacy. Pecan logs were, and still are, wads of caramel and nuts molded into the shape of logs, then rolled in a pecan mixture and wrapped in cellophane. They had them in all sorts of sizes, from the half-pounder to a real family size, which I could barely pick up.

When I was a kid, travelling in Theo's station wagon across the plains states, we used to go into every roadside diner we passed and buy tacky souvenir items. It was like a ritual: every forty miles or so we'd see one looming up on the side of the road, signs pointing the way, with at least half of the letters fallen off. Those were our favourites, the really tatty ones. I'd be sitting in the passenger seat alternately fiddling with the radio trying to get anything but the hog reports on the AM stations and staring out the window searching for familiar landmarks. On a clear day in the Midwest you can see for miles, nothing but vast stretches of unbroken wheat met in the far, far distance by the blue horizon. Miles roll by and the vista never changes; broken only by the occasional scarlet barn or gleaming silo. Then I thought it was horrible. Now I need it. In New York I got the worst cabin fever. I'd lie in bed at night, joints tingling with claustrophobia, aching to run and run and smell the pressed-down dirt of a ploughed field.

Anyway, we'd pull in, the two of us, and compete for the worst item. My all-time favourite was the clock, made out of a piece of cut tree trunk about two inches thick, then shellacked with a clear glaze, in the middle of which was glued a photograph of President Carter. It still hangs in Theo's study. And we'd play games, like Guess The Shape I'm Thinking Of, or What Would You Do If.

"What would you do if you could have a million dollars, but you would have to go blind?"

We wrestled with this one for a long time; I thought that if you had a million dollars you could pay someone to see for you.

"But what would be the point in having anything you wanted if you could never see any of it?"

Aunt Theo could always stump me. She'd play, eyes never leaving the road, cigarette clamped in the side of her mouth like a private detective, breathing out blue smoke, breathing in orange fire. Or she'd ask: which would you rather, eat nothing but sweets your whole life or never be able to have anything at all?

"If I ate sweets, couldn't I at least have some bread or something sometime?"

"Nope," she'd say, "nothing ever. Not even a lima bean." I loved lima beans. Reluctantly, I had to admit that I'd rather never eat sweets at all.

"Not me," she said, "let's go get a pecan log." So we would pull in, stretching our legs and smelling the empty air. I always checked the few cars in the parking lot carefully, hoping to recognize one someday, to see Sylvia stepping out of the passenger seat, reaching up to the clouds, stretching her body thin as a wire.

So I sent them things back to New York. I didn't try to explain anything; the air that changed the minute I crossed the state line into Iowa, the look of the women in all the roadside diners. I let them think what they wanted about the Midwest. I knew they wouldn't come here.

I pulled in on a soft summer twilight, feeling suddenly grubby and urban in my black city clothes. The sky was just fading to a soft heather-blue, sprinklers starting up with a hiss, the songs of crickets. From down the street I could hear the rhythmic thumping of a basketball, the thwang off the backboard. Aunt Theo's house looked dark and empty, the only one on the long street without a front light on. Summer in Kansas is like a state of suspended being: throughout the long hot days people sit immobilized, afraid to leave the comfort of their air-conditioning, or they lie on relatively cool floors feeling the sultry breeze of a fan drying the sweat that is always waiting just under the surface. I remember once during a long hot summer in high school staying in Finley I was rocking on the porch, swinging slowly with Jack. We were trying to identify stars. That was an infinitesimal rhythm of its own: back, forward, always up until the sky seemed like the ground itself and to look back down was vertigo. Rocking that way, my hand pointed at Orion, he leaned over suddenly and licked my cheek.

"Why did you do that?" I asked him, not really surprised, not really sexual.

"I wanted to taste salt," he said, and raised his hand to the heavens.

At nights people emerge. People you can't readily identify, who come up suddenly out of the dark, heralded by the stopping-short of locusts, the beginning again as they pass by. I like the summer dusk: you could be anybody. You never really know.

It took a long time to unload the U-Haul. When I was finished I went through the house, flicking on all the lights. It smelled empty, like a school in July. My possessions looked odd in the wide, open rooms of the house. That was one thing I had forgotten living in New York. In my old apartment I could touch the dull brick wall across the alley without even stretching. I lived by steps: five to the bedroom from the hall, three to the bed. One to the closet, then seven back into the living room. Four and a half to the kitchen, one complete circle around from refrigerator to oven. Eight back to the door. It took longer to do up all six locks than it did to cover the apartment.

Theo's house was open, there were no doors between the rooms. The dark wood floors creaked and groaned as all old houses do, expanding like a person in the cooling night air. Most of the furniture here was hers; the lawyer said I could do what I liked with it. At the moment all I could think of was closing the door behind me and going to bed. The whole drive I had been straining, almost pushing the car forward myself as I drove, and now I was here. I pulled the dust sheet off the battered green plaid sofa and sank down, suddenly unable to remember why I had come.

The kitchen looked the same: the row of copper pots gleamed dully over the window, the purple and blue tiles hadn't changed. When I was twelve I had picked them out myself: Theo decided that the kitchen needed "some sprucing up," and so we spent a whole summer doing it ourselves. Theo didn't much care for decorators or designers: she lived a solitary life, free from the worry of what people would think of her. I don't know how she did it; she would sweep through town, tall and imperious, dressed always in trousers: short-sleeved shirts in summer and spring, old sweaters in the colder months. She smoked, she drank a double bourbon before dinner every night, and she was the most beautiful woman I have ever seen. We all thought so; we'd follow her around, all the kids in the neighbourhood, as she made her rounds: library, drugstore, grocery. Every day, you could set your watch by it. I started to copy her style when I was in high school: pulled my hair back as tight as it would go, spent hours practising her steely look.

We selected everything for the kitchen, sitting together at the old silver-flecked formica table, fifty years of tea rings encircling one another.

"I don't know what possessed me," she said, looking around

her with mild astonishment at the 1950's yellow and pink decor. "Your grandfather, Sybil, he sent me a decorator, gave him to me for Christmas. Hmph, this is the best he could do?" Her arm, brandishing a long cigarette, jabbed at the items of most offence. "It's all got to go. All of it. We'll start anew." And so we sat, drinking instant coffee, Nescafe, which is firmly associated in my mind with that house, her house. My house.

I decided that we needed colour. "Lots of colour in warm tones." I had started art classes and was heavily into tones at the time. Theo just smiled, her hair dusted with the plaster that had come away when she ripped out the shelves. She didn't really care. I can see this now; it was just one more thing to take my mind off myself. I can't imagine that the purples, blues and bright canary-yellow accents I chose were any better to her than the old pink refrigerator. But for a summer we worked, listening to jazz on the radio, and at the end we inked our names on the wall behind the sink.

"For future generations," she announced, "it is always important to leave your mark."

Now, standing alone next to the window, letting the breeze from the open back door remind me of all this, I smiled. I could hear crickets, sprinklers, the swish of cars on the road. I breathed in the heavy night air, warmer than a sigh.

What Cherry Wants

Claire Hogg

Claire Hogg was born in 1967. She studied English Literature before moving to Greece where she taught for three years. She is currently working on a feature-length script.

Tableau. CHERRY is reclining, Cleopatra style, being fed black grapes by TYLER. Suddenly, she brushes him aside. She's had enough.

TYLER (vo)
Someone could be pouring out their heart to you, telling you how much they need you, how you're their world, and one day you realise that it doesn't touch you anymore. It's not that you're immune; just that it's all too much. There's only so much a cup can hold. You don't want to think about it, but maybe it's time to tip away the dregs. Give the cup time to dry, so that when it's next filled, you will notice the difference, and it will matter. Maybe.

NEW SCENE. *A large once-white studio. CHERRY is reclining naked on richly coloured material draped over a chaise longue on a small stage. She has dark hair, short and straight. She is surrounded by a crescent of twelve artists, half-hidden behind easels. Sound of charcoal scraping against paper, and CHERRY's light breathing. CU of CHERRY's right eyelid and lashes, the latter coated black. Her dark eye opens slowly to take in the artists. Draw out of this shot until we see all of CHERRY's face, cupped in TYLER's hands. TYLER's POV. TYLER leans forward and kisses CHERRY on each eyelid. She blinks slowly, but her eyes remain half-closed.*

CHERRY (vo)
Where are your cigarettes?

TYLER
In my back pocket.

(*CHERRY laughs. Camera draws away to reveal CHERRY and TYLER lying somewhere outside. It's very dark. CHERRY rolls off TYLER as he reaches into his back pocket and brings out a flattened packet of cigarettes, which he opens. We don't see details, more shadows and outlines. CU of TYLER's hand as he lifts the cigarette to his mouth. Move to MCU of TYLER in cold-looking room, dimly lit by a flickering TV screen. TYLER draws hard on the cigarette, takes it away from his mouth, and looks at it. (POV). TYLER laughs dryly, small clouds of smoke escaping from his mouth.*)

TYLER
No woman has ever squashed my cigarettes before.

(*TYLER's body moves jerkily as he laughs. CU of his wrist-watch. A plastic Mickey Mouse ticks from left to right, inanely. Black.*)

CHERRY (drawls)
Don't come to meet me until the class is over, Tyler.

(*CHERRY's POV in studio. Her gaze shifts to her right hand. Her nails are painted morello. Her right arm is cupped around her rounded stomach. MS of CHERRY from crescent. MCU as CHERRY darts her tongue lightly over her drying lips. Pan artists. There are eleven men and one woman. MS of female artist, WINIFRED. Her head is bowed, her hair scraped back roughly. We travel down her arm to her hand and the charcoal she is holding. MS of her drawing: an angry scorched area in the centre of the page. Move in closer and closer. Camera swings rapidly to sound of studio door opening. Enter TYLER, tallish and lanky. His dark blond hair hangs in an unkempt mop. The door clicks shut behind him. TYLER looks as if it's cold outside. His gaze hangs on CHERRY. WINIFRED turns to look at TYLER. WINIFRED's POV: she sees TYLER fiddle with his left cuff, and she smiles slightly to herself. Cut.*)

NEW SCENE. *CHERRY is wrapped in a dark cerise coat, the collar of which reaches up to her nose. TYLER's hands are thrust clenched into his pockets, his shoulders are hunched against the cold. Sound of boots stomping on ground frost and laboured breathing. CHERRY and TYLER briskly approach a church-like building with a studded wooden door. TYLER hauls the door open. Sound of voices and glasses clinking and fast salsa. TYLER allows CHERRY to enter, and follows. We watch the door close behind them. Cut.*

NEW SCENE. *A winter morning. Cold, bright light, a street of run-down shops with flats above. CHERRY moves quickly and lightly along the pavement, seemingly oblivious to the cold. She's wearing an unnecessarily large hat and is carrying a large paper bag and a bunch of keys. She halts before a battered door and inserts a key in the lock. A large black car creeps to a stop at the curb. An extremely portly man, MR SUGAR, emerges from the back seat, holding a tubular container. He coughs. CHERRY opens the door.*

> **MR SUGAR**
> Please, excuse me -

(CHERRY half turns, fails to recognize him.)

> **MR SUGAR**
> Tuesdays . . . life class?

> **CHERRY**
> Oh, Mr. Sugar, it's you.

> **MR SUGAR**
> I've finished my drawing – I'd like you to have a look at it.

(CHERRY's face relaxes into a smile as if this has happened before. She pushes the door open, and gestures MR SUGAR inside. CHERRY follows, looking back as she closes the door. She sees a uniformed man closing the car door after MR SUGAR. She closes the door. Black. Inside the flat, MR SUGAR leads, since CHERRY cannot get past. He pauses outside a door, open just enough to reveal a blue TV light.)

> **CHERRY**
> Not that room, Mr. Sugar.

(They enter a small but light kitchen. MR SUGAR looks awkward.)

> **CHERRY**
> Won't you sit down, Mr. Sugar?

> **MR SUGAR**
> Harold, please. Thank you.

(*CHERRY unbuttons her coat. MR SUGAR lowers himself on to a small wooden chair. The camera watches him fiddle with the container he's holding, until he eventually takes out the rolled paper.*)

CHERRY (os)
I didn't realise you were so close to finishing your drawing. Now you'll have to move seats to get a different angle. I don't think the rest of the class is ready for a new pose.

MR SUGAR
Yes, yes of course.

(*MR SUGAR looks up to see CHERRY in a Victorian hip bath, balanced on top of the kitchen table. CHERRY is totally covered up to her neck with fallen autumn leaves.*)

CHERRY
Is that the drawing Mr. – Harold? Do show me.

(*MR SUGAR's mouth works rapidly. He looks hot.*)

CHERRY
Mr. Sugar, is anything the matter? Would you like some water?

(*MR SUGAR sees CHERRY about to emerge from the tub, and shakes his head most definitely.*)

MR SUGAR
I'm sorry, my dear, I really have to be going. Forgive me.

(*MR SUGAR struggles to his feet. The camera watches him disappear down the stairs. CHERRY turns from emptying the paper bag.*)

CHERRY
But Mr. Sugar, your picture – oh!

(*The camera takes in the whole room. There is no bath. CHERRY is dressed, and she is holding the roll of paper. There is a crude but beautiful drawing of a bunch of spring flowers. Cut.*)

NEW SCENE. *In the church-like building. CU of band of smoke hanging over people's heads. CHERRY and TYLER are seated at a small table jammed in a corner. In front of CHERRY is a large wide-lipped balloon glass half-filled with red wine. TYLER has a colourless drink in a straight glass, and a small foil disc filled with large peanuts, roasted and salted still in their brick-maroon skins. Nervously he picks up nut after nut, rubbing each between the thumb and forefinger of his left hand until the skin drops away on to an ever increasing pile on the table.*

> **CHERRY**
> Didn't you eat before you came out, Tyler?

(CU of TYLER's mouth, chewing, small crystals of salt on his lips.)

> **TYLER**
> I don't like the way they look at you.

(CHERRY turns her glass thoughtfully, sighs. Camera follows CHERRY's gaze across the bar. The barman is pulling a pint. A woman begins to laugh.)

> **CHERRY**
>   I told you not to come so early *(pauses.)*
> Why don't you listen to me, Tyler?

(TYLER finishes the last peanut and draws his hand across his mouth.)

> **TYLER**
> Cherry –

(The woman's laughter is menacing. It grows louder and louder until it consumes the whole room. Suddenly it is cut short by the tinkling of glass splintering. Strobe of TYLER turning towards sound, away from CHERRY. MS of laughing woman. She is WINIFRED. She's excessive, threatening. We get the feeling she's laughing at TYLER. MS of piece of broken glass on the floor under a table, slowly filling with deep red drips. Move to CU of drips sending out ripples. Dissolve to portrait shot of CHERRY, her lips frozen on the brink of drinking. CHERRY is transfixed by WINIFRED.)

> **CHERRY**
> Tyler, I love what I do.

NEW SCENE. STUDIO. *CHERRY is standing on stage, arms stretched out level with shoulders, legs planted firmly apart. We see her from standpoint behind crescent, to the right. Slide focus to foreground. MR SUGAR is to our right, seated right of WINIFRED. His dimpled hands are working on a border for his as yet undrawn sketch. The border is made up of tiny bunches of black grapes, almost stencilled in effect. Shift to left, leaving only a slice of MR SUGAR to screen right. WINIFRED has sketched an arm, sculptural in essence, diagonally left to right on the paper. We see only the shoulder and elbow of her drawing. CU of CHERRY's head, neck and shoulders, with intimation of outstretched arms.*

NEW SCENE. *Return to WINIFRED. She uses a small knife to begin to cut out the arm She starts on the inside, moving up to the shoulder, round then down. As she gets past the elbow, MR SUGAR drops his charcoal, and WINIFRED's knife slips. The arm is severed, and floats down to the floor. All that remains are a fist and a wrist, wearing a Mickey Mouse watch. Black.*

NEW SCENE. *Tableau. CHERRY, pallid, reclining, her left arm thrown dramatically over her forehead. TYLER dabs at her inner left arm, which is bleeding from an invisible cut just below the elbow. She moans gently. He covers the cut with a salmon Bandaid. Exit TYLER. Enter MR SUGAR. MR SUGAR presents CHERRY with a large round raspberry lollipop on a stick. He pats her head.*

> **MR SUGAR (soothing)**
> Don't cry, my child, don't cry.

NEW SCENE. *Early spring. TYLER is digging a hole. It's just big enough for a person. The ground is hard, and TYLER pauses frequently to blow on his gloveless hands. At one stage, when the hole is nearly finished, TYLER's foot slips on the spade. He begins to fall. Black.*

NEW SCENE. STUDIO. *Bright lighting makes everything seem scruffier and more drab. LS of stage, empty save a wooden chair. The crescent has gone. Even from a distance, his size makes MR SUGAR recognizable. He is on all fours in front of and facing stage, intently drawing something on paper on floor. Cut.*

NEW SCENE. *CU of TYLER's watch. Draw out. Reveal watch placed with strap stretched out, lying on earth. MS of TYLER heading towards hole. In his arms are four large stones. He reaches the edge of the hole, puts down the stones with care, and leans over the edge of the hole. TYLER's POV – his watch at the bottom of a large hole. Sound of a cuckoo. Sound stops abruptly as TYLER stands back to review his work. Picks up Thermos and opens it. Pours remaining drink. Sips, spits, and empties contents of cup on to earth. Wipes out cup with shirt tail.*

NEW SCENE. *Exterior cafe/cake shop. Rows of pink iced buns fill the window. Interior. CHERRY with WINIFRED. CHERRY is drinking pink milkshake through a straw. WINIFRED looks at her watch which has a serious, plain face.*

> **WINIFRED**
> Hurry now Cherry. Time to go home.

(CHERRY looks petulant, but hurries.)

NEW SCENE. HOLE. *TYLER finishes placing the four stones, then straightens up. MR SUGAR's flower picture has been weighed down over the mound of earth which now fills the hole.*

NEW SCENE. STUDIO. *L/MS of MR SUGAR, standing on stage facing camera. Proudly holding excellent sketch of CHERRY before him. He smiles. Sound of CHERRY laughing.*

> **WINIFRED**
> That's enough now Cherry.

(CHERRY continues to laugh, almost becoming hysterical.)

> **WINIFRED**
> I said, that's enough.

(Sound stops dead. Camera lingers for a second on MR SUGAR.)

FADE OUT

Extract from

The Shifting Surface of Desire; A Life of the painter Johannes Vermeer of Delft

Brian Howell

Brian Howell was born in London. Since graduating from Manchester University he has worked in Hungary and the Czech Republic. Since 1990 he has published various short stories. The idea for the extracted novel grew out of a long-term interest in seventeenth century Dutch painting.

His father was two persons even within the same place, but only when Reynier took him one day to the market on business did Johannes become aware of this second person, the one who was attempting to impart knowledge to the eight-year-old.

A passing trader, a stranger to Reynier, had set up with an assortment of wares, among these the silk known as caffa. Johannes noticed how Reynier caught the man's eye, how his father's hand delved into the folds of the material he knew so well.

The boy was not supposed to touch but did so, oblivious to censure.

"Johannes!" Reynier shouted.

Johannes continued to worry the cloth. He had known the feeling before but this time his investigation took a different form, one that tried to follow the pattern that one minute was there, the next was not.

He looked up at his father. He was seeing him too in a new light; his body was now a contradiction, a bulky torso like a bursting sack of grain, short legs that more than matched the power and threat of the upper half, and the hands. These hands were huge like his own, and till now were the only ones in the family to caress the merchants' silks, to make their invisible inventory of warp and weft as they assessed texture. The same hands were capable of hoisting barrels or suspending the child's life over an ocean of fear should he swerve from the path that was good. Yet Reynier never hit his child; there had never been occasion.

"Two guilders."

Reynier gave the trader's offer some thought, then, on the point of turning, decided to buy the cloth. But Reynier's thoughts had for once not been engaged completely with financial matters. He was thinking of other possibilties. He now saw the child truly. The child was a quiet but involving companion. The space that had imposed itself between them during the boy's earliest years was now collapsing, and Reynier was glimpsing something of his world, as mysterious and infinite as the new constellations that were being talked of.

Johannes recognized a change in Reynier: during the walk home, his father was suddenly taken with explaining the details of the material, how it was made, its advantages over other cloths. Johannes had never known him so talkative.

As there were two fathers, there were two worlds, indoors and outdoors, and it seemed often that there was no connection between the two. The indoor world, which dominated, was defined by dark. Even inside was never completely inside, because line and form always conspired to direct the eye into the deeper space. Doors led to other doors, pictures to other pictures; mirrors, which resembled pictures, threw the boy back from where he had come into another, framed world.

At the centre of the indoor world was the inn proper, where elegant forms, muffled by pipe smoke and whispers, would move in a blur to their customary positions, releasing an expression of thanks or even a coin to the young Johannes as he brought them their drinks.

Plain, thin-faced and still unmarried, his sister Gertruy would draw the men's attention, even the occasional officer's. Perhaps Reynier's vigilance over his male customers and his violent history made them keep their distance and admiring glances to themselves. Perhaps his concern for his cherished painters led him to neglect her prospects. But it was her goodness, her good intentions that they saw.

It was January three years before, when they had run The Flying Fox in the Voldersgracht behind the Market. A wind from the sea was scything through the narrow streets of the town, and the ice by the woods was a closed eye which could at any moment open and swallow up the drifting, cheering forms. Reynier was even then sturdy, compact, thundering around on skates, the best of the hockey players. A sudden collision, and three forms are on the ice in a clap of laughter. So they remain until a question is asked: where is Reynier?

In the near distance by the trees Reynier and another figure stand, knives glistening like lizards' tongues, and before Reynier's friends can draw themselves up, the other man is upon the innkeeper. Reynier's parries only inspire the assailant, and it is doubtful that he will survive the attack.

Reynier's friends gather around the attacker, who will not desist from his mission, and they rain down on him with their hockey clubs until he is on the ice, his legs askew. Reynier is now restrained from what he considers a just retribution, and it takes all three of them to draw him away. In the inn it is finally divulged that the culprit, a captain in the army, had commented on the reputation of the establishment that Reynier kept and the role of his daughter, Gertruy. His friends laugh off the accusation for what it is: unfounded. And it seems that all is settled.

Yet in the night the five-year-old is woken to witness a scene that will remain indelible: his father on the stairs, much enraged by his own drink, being held back by Johannes's mother, Digna and his sister, Gertruy. This time the knife that shines even in near dark is paraded against an absent foe, and the child hides his head between his knees as he squats against the prison-bar railings of the landing. The father is in time persuaded to exercise caution and go by the way of the law. Johannes cannot remember whether he saw this final stage but in the morning Reynier is his everyday self, as if nothing has happened to disturb his ambitions for respectability.

The day they moved to the Mechelen Inn on the Market Square, Johannes saw a new Delft. The New Church and the Town Hall to either side, whilst never crowding out the unending sky, defined the narrow compass of his visible world. He need never leave the Square. No, he did not ever wish to. He would be happy to go with his father forever to solemn meetings where documents were signed and expressions exchanged in an air of perfunctory civic satisfaction. Or to follow Gertruy to the market, her face dipped into its collar as if the attention she did not seek nor gain pushed her gaze inward.

It was on one of those early days after the move that he saw Catharina Bolnes for the first time.

She was standing with her mother and a gentleman, looking impatiently out of her bonnet as if to protest against the restriction of this frame on her view. Her mother's expression was severe but respectful towards the man. Perhaps in that petulant swivel of hers the young girl saw Johannes for a moment, linked to his sorrowful sister as fast as she herself was to her mother.

Gertruy noticed his sudden lagging behind, and looked up for only the third or fourth time during their walk.

"Johannes, don't stare."

"Who is she?"

"Maria Thins. Can't you see she's talking to that heretic priest?"

"No, not her, the . . ."

Gertruy let out a rare puff of irritation. "Her daughter, Catharina, I should think. What do you want with her? They wouldn't talk to the likes of us even if we converted."

"Why should we convert?"

"Johannes," Gertruy huffed, shaking her head and pulling her brother along roughly.

One evening Johannes was told to stop serving and go up to his father's work room.

The door was open. Silently, Johannes approached his father as he crouched over his loom. Before the boy could surprise him, Reynier stopped his weaving and turned around to reach for the sketches he had made in preparation. He handed them to Johannes.

The boy's attention was equally divided between the drawn designs and the cloth.

"Which do you prefer?"

Johannes looked from Reynier to the drawing, then to the cloth, and back to his father.

"What do you want to be? A weaver, or an artist?"

Johannes's tentative finger reached towards the loom. Reynier showed no reaction. At the last moment, as if it were a game between father and son, Johannes chose the sketches, and giggled.

A year later Johannes made the first of his daily trips to the painter Cornelis Daemen Rietwijck's academy on the nearby Voldersgracht to learn drawing.

Then there was Digna. And her tales.

Her stories of her brother Balthens and her father Balthasar's adventures interleaved his earliest days, sewing up the languorous gaps with imagined scenes of activity. Even when his mind and body were full of other things, the stories were always in the background somewhere, never suffocating, but watching over him.

Johannes's grandfather and uncle had been counterfeiters. They had forged coins. Balthens had been in prison, but he had risen above his misdeeds to invent a machine that had saved Holland from the wrath of the Spanish.

One afternoon Reynier walked into the kitchen to hear once more his wife recounting the familiar story. He lost his temper and threw a faince dish against the wall. "What rubbish are you speaking again? Do you want the boy to grow up thinking he is descended from criminals?"

"Talented criminals at any rate," she retorted as she picked up the pieces, keeping her eyes lowered. At such moments Johannes felt their life to be as fragile as that ruined piece of crockery. And the feeling of potential destruction was all the keener as the child anticipated his mother's next words. She was afraid of Reynier, to be sure, but she would not hold back when she deemed her husband to be unjust. On this occasion Reynier did not give her the opportunity.

"He has all the talent he needs in those hands of his."

All three looked at those broad wedges of flesh, which in their seeming awkwardness promised so little. At that moment Reynier looked up, and smiled, and the heaviness in the air was broken. In the middle of this Gertruy walked into the room to find the trio laughing. Her smile, which was a beautiful one, soon turned into a laugh too.

Johannes had never seen anyone dressed like Rietwijck. At first the old man's breeches and long coat frightened him, but he was to become an ally.

The other, older pupils, who read in his dress a liking for the French style, would sometimes hum a French tune, but Rietwijck's ability to locate the culprits and issue summary punishment seemed to Johannes almost supernatural.

Johannes, impatient to draw, made slow progress in arithmetic, geometry, and astronomy. Yet his ability to absorb Aristotle and Alberti baffled the teacher.

After lessons, Gerrit, carrot-topped and muscular, and his brother Simon, blond and skinny, would try to block the young apprentice's exit, lurching from one side of the alley to the other as Johannes ran their interweaving gauntlet.

When they finally succeeded in taking from Johannes's bag a sketch he had made of Mechelen, its size out of all proportion to the other houses and the New Church on the Square, Gerrit and Simon sank down on the cobbled stones in a fit of laughter. Their mockery hurt more than their worst beatings.

The rug was draped across a table and a plate of fruit placed on it. Johannes's attention was fixed more by the pattern of the rug than by the light cast on the fruit. He was hungry.

Once, Gerrit had taken a cluster of grapes, destroying the composition Johannes had laboured over for hours. Rietwijck had not noticed on that occasion. Today Johannes had spent so long on the detail of the rug that the bowl had wandered to the edge of the table. Now he was faced with a mess. The old man stood in disbelief as he looked at Johannes's work.

"What is that? It inhabits no space that I know of."

It was true, he now saw.

Rietwijck continued his inspection of the others' work. "Excellent, excellent, excellent, excellent." Each praise exploded in Johannes a small bomb of humiliation.

I will never draw, I won't learn numbers, I hate numbers, he tried to convince himself, but his teacher returned to him and replaced the sheet. Rietwijck looked at his timepiece, then dismissed the others.

Gerrit and Simon hovered awhile, reluctant to leave only because their after-lesson fun had been spoiled. Rietwijck kept Johannes for another hour without charge until he had produced a satisfactory rendition.

The man was laid on the rack, his arms and feet extending to the four corners as if these supported the very construction. He was no longer whole yet his body had never felt so complete in its purpose.

The sheriff gave the order for the 200-pound weights to be lowered, then lifted, and Johannes looked on, fixed as much by horror as by the enclosing row of soldiers. How would his uncle recover to save the nation? Did they not know about his talents?

The weights were lifted momentarily, only to be lowered once more, and Johannes heard in his uncle's scream the rush of cascading waves which would engulf them all if the officials persisted in their unjust intentions.

But the moan grew ever louder until it swallowed everyone in the room, and Johannes woke to the taste of his own sea-salty tears. Gertruy was there, comforting him as ever. Through a gap he saw the half-open door and heard mocking voices from the inn downstairs.

"Who will save Uncle Bathens?" he said, still half in his nightmare. "Who will save Sas van Gent?"

"They are saved," Gertruy said harshly, but the harshness was directed at her mother for filling the boy's head to such effect as this. "They are saved."

As she tucked him in, Reynier appeared at the door, filling out the threshold like a dark spilling liquid. For a moment she had feared a drunken customer. "Downstairs," was all he said.

The night visions found their counterparts in a cluster of incidents that occurred shortly after the move to Mechelen. At their centre was one evening when Johannes was serving in the inn along with Gertruy.

He had been aware that since the move a number of things had changed: some of them palpable, such as the addition in recent days of a painting, an old-fashioned merry company of elegant ladies and gentlemen, which Reynier had proudly hung behind the bar. And a distant relative had on occasion come to play the guitar. Other changes were harder to define.

Yet the usual combinations were present: the sweet smell of smoke that always stung his eyes; the trio of good-for-nothings who played cards and hunched over coals to light their pipes; two fishwives; the framemaker Anthony van der Wiel and his brothers; the local baker; Itge Jacobs and another woman. In short, the locals from the Fox, good and bad, had followed them to Mechelen.

On that particular evening Johannes noticed some newer customers, a group of well-dressed young men, one of them a soldier. After his return to the inn from a short meal break, Johannes had good reason to study the man more closely. The soldier, who sat by a window, had his back turned away from Johannes. Sitting across the table from him, to the boy's astonishment, was Gertruy. The soldier's companions had shifted to the end of the table. As Johannes walked by them, the soldier's red jacket seemed to dominate everything else in the inn. Gertruy barely noticed her brother as he passed by, taking tankards to the card players.

"Yes, and there'll be trouble yet," he caught one saying.

"Soon he'll only let in the likes of them," said another, tilting his head in the direction of the soldier and the well-dressed men.

It was the mood of the tavern that had changed. Johannes continued on to the fishwives. As he approached, they curtailed their talk abruptly, and gave their orders. They did not smile in their usual happy-go-lucky way. He went up to Itge, who, engrossed in her latest commentary on the state of the town's morals, did not notice his approach. "Bits of flesh, they say, have fallen out of her. She'll not

Brian Howell

be stepping into any young man's house for a while, I shouldn't wonder." As she saw him, she drew in her breath and looked around, as if about to choke. The other woman ordered sharply.

At the bar, waiting for the orders, Johannes now saw the change more concretely. He became aware that there were not only fewer customers in the inn, but that the composition, which normally formed a whole, albeit a raucous one, was now broken up. Limbs, the sway of bodies, the directions of people's gazes, no longer formed a harmony. The place was taut with uncertainty. Yet Reynier and Digna showed no sign of being aware of this.

Johannes stood there for a moment, disgusted by the lewdness of everything. Why would Gertruy not look at him? Would the soldier take her away from Anthony, from the inn, from him? He almost asked his mother, but he could not find the words. Reynier noticed Johannes dawdling, but he was not angry. Digna passed her son two tankards. When he had served the beers, he went over to Anthony and his brothers. They too were mumbling with discontent.

"It's not true, I tell you. If you're my brothers, you'll know that when I say it," he was saying in a shrill voice. Despite this, he managed a smile for Johannes. This reassured the boy, but as he moved away, he heard Gertruy's name come from one of them.

"Then why else would the soldier come here for her?"

His hands shaking, and the empty glasses rattling, Johannes went up to his mother and buried his face in her chest. The realization had come suddenly, sweeping him away on a wave of humiliation so that tears came and made his eyes burn even more than usual.

"What is it, son?"

"They're saying things about Gertruy."

"No, what kind of things?"

"I don't know. Who's that man she's with?"

"That's the Captain. He's our friend."

"What's she doing?"

"She's not working tonight."

His fears were almost assuaged, were beginning to disappear, when they were revived and given a definite form.

Itge Jacobs, now openly drunk, walked over to Gertruy and made her accusation public. Perhaps spurred on by the unusual attention that Gertruy was receiving from the Captain, Itge began to fawn on the soldier, one minute falling against him, the other threatening immediately to fall back. This left the gentleman with no choice but to catch her by the arm.

"That's it, wonderful," Itge said, surprisingly in control all of a sudden, "You don't want to play with them that's had pieces . . ."

At this Anthony stood up in a rage, his brothers attempting to hold him back. The fishwives gave approving smiles.

"Enough!" Reynier's exclamation thundered across the inn. "Out, woman. Enough. This is a respectable house, and will only serve those worthy of it."

Reynier now took the drunken Itge by the waist and thrust her out onto the street. Inside, he turned and cast his eyes across the cowering company, pointed at Itge's companion, then at the card players.

"And you, and you, and you. Out. Respectable people only. This is an end to gossip. I have a business to run."

The card players, the fishwives and the woman filed out sheepishly. The only words Reynier spoke after this were to his son.

"A beer to everyone in the house."

Some days after that evening Johannes accompanied his father to the notary, Willem de Langue. It was not the first time that he had been on this short trip, but this occasion gained a special place in his childhood.

They would normally have approached de Langue's via the Great Market Square, but on this day Reynier had picked Johannes up from Rietwijck's in the Voldersgracht and was intending to continue to the bottom of the street, thus avoiding going onto the crowded Square. As they walked along the canal he noticed his father's quietness.

Johannes stopped to look at the tower of the New Church, which seemed at this moment to lean and threaten to fall. He felt a need to go by the usual route, through the Square. He reached out a hand, but Reynier was gone. He walked on to the corner, calling out for his father. Now, the buttresses of the church were the sprung legs of a giant insect.

Looking round, he saw Reynier coming out of the tailor's, shaking hands. Johannes ran, into his father's arms. Johannes pulled him back into the Square.

"Johannes? What's the matter?"

"Why didn't you stop for me? The tower's falling."

Reynier smiled. "The tower falling, eh? We'll see." They walked into the Square, and stood looking up at the tower and its spires. "You see? It's not falling, Johannes. As long as it's there, you know where you are. You know where north and south are."

Johannes nodded, uncertain but calmed.

They walked to the other side of the Square, where they turned left along the Oude Langendijck till they reached de Langue's office on the cattle market. The building was slightly wider than most in Delft, as if to suggest its importance over the adjacent residences. They were met by de Langue's secretary, who asked them to wait. During this time, Johannes, thinking of the events in the inn, said,

"Father?"

"Yes, son."

"Who was the soldier? Did he come for Gertruy?"

"Where did you get that idea from?"

"Anthony didn't look happy."

Reynier cleared his throat, then reached for his handkerchief. Johannes noticed it was new and very white.

"He was . . . interested. You needn't worry yourself."

"Will Gertruy marry Anthony?"

"In time, Johannes, in time."

Johannes sat there, puzzled, but before he had a chance to pursue the subject, the secretary came out and ushered them in. As they entered, there came polite mutterings indicating that some matter of great weight had finally been concluded.

Behind the desk stood the portly de Langue. His expression was stern but not impenetrable, and a stranger seeing him for the first time might have detected a kindly disposition.

Around the desk, as if radiating unequally from the document placed there, stood four figures, some of whom Johannes had seen in the inn. The man who stood nearest to the document and signed first was addressed by de Langue as de heer Jan Baptista van Fornenburgh, and was followed in turn by de heers Pieter van Groenewegen and Balthasar van der Ast, then, finally, by Reynier.

Johannes held on to his father's hand and watched him slowly, thoughtfully, sign, *Reynier Jansz. Vermeer, alias Vos*. A small chuckle went round the group as they saw the boy shadow his father with curiosity.

On the way home, Johannes, attempting to keep up with his father's enlivened step, asked, "What does it mean? Are we now called Vermeer, father?"

Reynier stopped suddenly, and lowered himself so that his head was level with his son's, and he grasped hold of the boy, revelling in the diminutive mirror-image of that jutting jaw and wide mouth that seemed so open, so impressionable.

"Yes, it means that we have made a change. We are now Vermeer or, if you wish, van der Meer. We are of the sea. Our fate is linked to it like that of the seven States. And," he glanced in the direction of the nearby Flying Fox Inn, "we have moved from that place. For good."

The days with Rietwijck sank under a vast perse cloud weighted down with numbers, lines, triangles, projections. Johannes was not a prize pupil. He forced himself to adequacy. He did not understand, yet he was fascinated, and perhaps it was this that tempered Rietwijck's otherwise impatient nature. And Johannes's drawing had improved little. At one stage he had been in danger of being overtaken even by slow Adriaen, who Rietwijck kept on more out of pity than for any other reason.

However, Johannes had formed a friendship with this boy, who lived in the house, and this gave Johannes justifiable reason to stay awhile after lessons. It was on one of these occasions that Johannes took to browsing through Rietwijck's modest library.

There were perhaps twenty books in all, mostly in Latin. He could by now decipher the titles and purpose of most of these, and one quarto volume, which had the word FRISIO in gold lettering on the spine, caught his attention.

Rietwijck, who was involved in a complicated operation to repair the blinds, looked around momentarily to see the young boy stretching for this book on one of the higher shelves. Rietwijck was about to help him, but Johannes succeeded in inching it out until it fell into the safety of his grasp. Rietwijck, his moustache twitching with curiosity at Johannes's precocity, decided to say nothing, seeing that the book was undamaged. His pupil became quietly lost in a network of diagrams and engravings. The master recognized the book immediately: de Vries's *Perspective*.

The teacher observed the boy's raptness. The fact that the text was in Latin did not seem to diminish his engagement with it. Rietwijk recalled his own first perusal of the book, in his youth. It had been as if he had entered a strange world where everything that was subject to definition by straight lines was demonstrated. Always a grid of boxes or tiles was the measure of space and proportion, whether it was a room, a square, or some architectural fancy, and where points could be connected to the horizon they were connected, and these joined at eye level in beautiful harmony; even rounded figures were subject to these concentrations and convergences of line.

Rietwijck noticed where Johannes's gentle turning of the pages had come to a halt; the teacher knew that he could cough or cast a shadow across the boy at this moment and it would not disturb him. What could his pupil make of this drawing, an example of two distance points which flanked a central vanishing point? He was tempted to question the boy, but decided for once to let his enjoyment of such work remain innocent. There would be time. He left the boy on his own and went off to light the candles in the rest of the downstairs rooms.

Johannes continued to study the network of diamond tiles demonstrated in the diagram until there was barely any light to see by, even when he went over to the window. It was in this circumstance that he came across another engraving that he had overlooked at the very beginning of the book, but soon after he fell into a deep sleep.

The eye pulsed and swirled about a hidden axis. Pyramids radiated about its centre and travelled to the four corners, elongated by fixed points, as if to form a buckled, imperfect canvas. These were areas of peripheral vision, and they were pinned down by the intersecting cross of one sharp, demanding focus, where the sight seen was overwhelming. In the swirl of scenes – knife on flesh, blood on ice, restricting bars, racked limbs, the warm, comforting bosom of his mother– his thoughts floated away, and swam to the edge of vision once more.

Rietwijck's gentle pat on the back brought him suddenly out of the flood of his thoughts.

"We shall make a painter of you yet, though it will not be within my time with you."

Johannes, sleepy as he still was, found it hard to pay attention, and his teacher seemed disappointed by the boy's lack of response to the compliment.

"Now, boy, go. You have work to do in the tavern."

By the end of the year Rietwijck's simple instruction gave way to that of two local masters, and it seemed that nothing would come of the months he had spent poring over the book by de Vries and another by Dürer. The first of his mentors, van Aelst, showed little interest in him beyond doing what was necessary to repay the debts he had accumulated in Reynier's inn. He already had his favourites, and his world was as distant and ungraspable as the still lifes at which he excelled.

The apprenticeship did not outlast the debt, and not even the acquisition of one of van Aelst's paintings, which Reynier could not sell, could satisfy the innkeeper. Sensing Johannes's mute protest, Reynier decided to take on the extra expense of another master. The impending transition was not a smooth one, and knowledge of it came to the young artist in the form of another dispute.

Johannes arrived back at the inn already shaken. For the second time he had seen her, and his stomach was unsettled with anxiety. This time she appeared even haughtier than the first, but she was not with her mother; the lady who accompanied her was perhaps her aunt. Did she see him? He could not know. Her custom of casting her eyes down was more pronounced than before, but he had time to register the deep-set sockets of her eyes and her broad features. Yet her distance was not just one of attitude. To the twelve-year-old she was already a woman. He had rarely seen anyone of such bearing and dressed in such a manner except in the finest paintings. She already wore a jacket and dress of material the like of which his father had never woven. And Gertruy certainly did not possess clothing of such quality.

It seemed the source of the dispute was not financial.

In the main kitchen Digna sat with her hands dipped between her large thighs. Johannes entered, catching her in mid-sentence, so light was his tread.

". . . because the man's a Catholic, and that'll be the ruination of our son."

"What rot you talk, woman. Even Rembrandt had a Catholic master."

"Yes, and look at the result."

"Result? When did you see a Rembrandt?"

She turned her face to the light, the sun's stencil of lattice casting a stretched diamond of deep blue across her apron. "I've heard," she answered almost under her breath.

"Heard," Reynier repeated contemptuously. "It's the first I've heard you know anything about art."

"I can remember days when you talked of nothing else, even weaving. Don't you think I listened? Don't you think I wanted to learn more?" She paused awhile for breath, then went on, "Reynier, your son sees deeper than you, than any of us. Do you want him to hide his talents behind this . . . these biblical whatnots?"

"Listen, Digna, we're talking about the training. That's basic to every artist. Bramer can guarantee that."

"If my father . . ."

At this dawning of an old argument, Reynier's body tensed, so that his stumpy muscles showed momentarily through his shirt, his whole frame seeming to prepare for some impact. It was only now that they became aware of the child, standing in the oblong of shadow cast by the half-open door, through the low, consistent waves of sound which were for all his attempt to cover them unmistakeable: their son had heard everything and he was standing there crying.

Before either Digna or Reynier could move, Johannes had run out of the house, back out into the dark, his progress ghosted by canals which seemed to run with him and follow him everywhere.

From the bottom of the Great Market, he ran along the canal, then cut across a bridge, to the south of the town, then another bridge, the light fading all the while. He did not dare to look back.

He continued through the last quarter of houses until he reached the town wall. Though there was the wall, he could cross a bridge into open fields. Where was he to go? There was no mystery beyond this point. He knew where he was when he saw the towering windmill by the Schiedam Gate.

He had rarely visited the harbour except with his mother or father, and he had been warned of its dangers. Of tides suddenly engulfing the wharf and sweeping away hapless children, of unscrupulous men who would take a child on board a ship never to be seen again, of the women who patrolled the area for no respectable reason.

There was little light from the street lanterns here, but a ship was being loaded. A middle-aged man was overseeing the work, and a woman was walking by, glancing sidelong at the men as she passed them. Then she returned, and did the same again. After some time, when the stevedore seemed to be happy with his men, she approached him, not saying a word. He spent some time assessing her, then took her by the arm, pulling harshly.

Johannes drew back into the shadow of the Gate, where he had been standing till now. There was a knowing laugh in the distance from the sailors, along with a few envious grunts. He almost fell backwards when he realized that the stevedore was coming towards the Gate with the woman. He drew further back into the shadow, holding his breath.

The man stopped and pushed her against the wall. They hadn't seen him. The woman demanded money, and with a barely suppressed groan he passed some coins to her. Johannes could see nothing. He wanted to leave but if he were to move now, he might be thought by the sailor to be spying on them, held up to ridicule in front of the whole ship, or perhaps even taken away.

He heard cloth rip, then the rising and falling tones of the two invisible figures barely four feet from him, the sound of rough cloth against rougher brick, the man's sudden snort and a final bluster and sigh. All the while Johannes tried to summon the image of Catharina, as if by an act of repudiation, but only the barest outline appeared. Then this moment of seeming calm was broken by the sound of a thump like a hand hitting a sack of grain.

He heard the woman slump down to the ground as the man walked off. "Bastard," he heard her mutter as she tried to stifle tears, then, quite beyond his belief, she said, "I know you're there, love. Don't be afraid." Johannes started to move away, gradually but determinedly. When he was perhaps ten feet out, she emerged, her bodice hanging limply where it had been torn. He could not make out the colour in the light. But not even the brief sight of her full, milky-white breasts could distract him from the sight of her face, a beautiful one, distorted only by ridges of red around her eyes, cheeks, and mouth. She withdrew, a half-smile falling back into a scowl of disappointment.

He walked for twenty yards lost in thought, shame and pity, at one point almost stumbling down the bank into the canal. As he pulled himself up, he hit something hard and abrasive, smelling of sweat, and started to run before he even thought to look up. But the hand had caught him by the wrist.

Slowly, the realization came, the familiar touch, the attractive force that brought him round like a planet. He was staring at the moon face of his father where argent tears slipped timidly from the corners of his eyes. Would he hit him now, for the first time?

Hand in hand, they walked in silence back to the inn, the son's mind playing back this unlikely sequence of events. The subject of the evening's argument was smothered by welcoming relief. Of his encounter he could and would say nothing except to Gertruy.

The Colonel's Birthday

Charles Lambert

Charles Lambert was born in London in 1968. After living in Paris and writing pop lyrics for his group *Chazza & The Frisbees*, he is now working on a novel and a feature script.

INT. TURKEY PROCESSING FACTORY. *Female workers are coming to the end of an eight-hour night-shift at the conveyor belts. SAM and GINA, both in their mid twenties, chuck the last few turkey heads into the bin as the machine shuts down. A man, also dressed in white overalls with blood spattered across the front, briskly sweeps the floor around them. SAM and GINA walk out to the locker room. Their faces are pasty, with heavy bags under their eyes.*

> **GINA**
> Oh shit. I mustn't be late getting the kids off mum.
> She's going into town for the day.
>
> **SAM**
> She's good like that, your mum.
>
> **GINA**
> Yes. (*Pausing to reflect*)
> Yes, she is. She's fucking brilliant. Never says a word.
> She just understands, 'ow it's all different from when she
> brought us up.
>
> **OTHER GIRL 1**
> Bye Sam.
>
> **SAM**
> Bye.
>
> **OTHER GIRL 2**
> You out tonight?

SAM
Not tonight.

OTHER GIRL 2
Go on, treat yourself. *(Pause).* You alright?

SAM
I'm fine. *(Forcing a smile)* Well, I might see you later. See how I feel when I wake up.

(The other girls leave. SAM and GINA are alone in the locker room.)

GINA
So, will I see you tonight?

(SAM shrugs. GINA puts her arm around her shoulders and they sit down together on one of the benches.)

GINA
Do you want me to come home with you?

SAM
Now, it's not often I get an offer like that.

GINA
No! You know what I mean.

(Suddenly SAM gets up and moves towards the door. GINA follows.)

SAM
No, that's kind. He's been much better lately. But yesterday he didn't get out of bed. I never know what to expect when I get back. It's been bad enough getting him out of bed to sign on.

GINA
Perfect! If you're having to look after him you can claim an attendance allowance.

SAM
Since when did 'invalid' cover a depressed alcoholic?

GINA
Perhaps if he has a proper breakdown, then you could claim something.

(They walk down the passage which takes them into the administrative area of the plant. There are posters advertising Colonel Rooster's products.)

SAM
Part of me hates him. I loathe him when he sits there feeling sorry for himself, pile of empty tins and ash building up beside the bed. That really fucks me off. *(Softer)* And then at other times I just think he's tried so hard, Gina. And I think if it had happened to me I'd be doing just the same. *(Pausing outside a door)*. I've got to collect my overtime from Scrooge. Couldn't be more needed at the moment.
I'll ring you later if I'm up for somethingthis evening.

(SAM knocks at the door.)

GINA
Oh Christ, it's already ten past. See you later love. I'll speak to you later, bye.

(GINA presses on down the corridor. MR ROBINS opens the door.)

SAM
Mr.Robins, I've come about my cheque.

ROBINS
Ah, just the person I was hoping to see. Is Gina with you?

SAM
No.

ROBINS
That's not her I hear disappearing down the corridor?

SAM
I don't think so.

(ROBINS sticks his head round the door and yells.)

ROBINS
Gina, get back into this office now. *(Silence. ROBINS sings out the following, pausing slightly between each sentence.)* You'll be signing on Monday morning. Four weeks to Christmas. Think of the kiddies. Their expectant little faces looking out for Santa. *(ROBINS mockingly adopts child's voice.)*
Where're our presents, Mummy? Why hasn't Father Christmas come this year, Mummy? Why don't you give us presents like all the other parents?

(Shadow and light further down the empty corridor. It is obvious that GINA has been listening. She steps partially into view. ROBINS' child voice becomes more hysterical.)

Why hasn't Daddy brought some presents home? Mummy, why don't we have a Daddy?

GINA
Mr.Robins, not tonight, please. I'm in a hurry. A real hurry. I've got to pick up my kids.

ROBINS
Colonel Rooster's favourite little chicks aren't going to let him down, are they? No, not tonight. The very night he's bought them both presents. You know what happens to bad little chicks, don't you? *(Adopting voice of a turkey/chicken.)* Oh, Colonel, no. No! Not us for supper. Please, Colonel, not us. Not between two tender pieces of juicy matured cheddar coated with mouthwatering breadcrumbs. Not me. Please, Colonel. I've got my children to think about.

(ROBINS goes inside his office and they follow.)

CUT TO INT. ROBINS' OFFICE
Posters advertising turkey products (Colonel Rooster – from Freezer to Microwave in Just Ten Mins, Mmmmmm, Yummmy) charts on walls showing productivity charts, factors of production; labour and capital, etc.

ROBINS

I've got your pay cheque, Sam. And your overtime cheque.

SAM (*becoming nervous.*)

Oh, great. I'm rather in need of that at the moment. I just wanted to put one or two things to you both before you rush off.

(*ROBINS goes to desk drawer and removes something which he slips into his pocket. He goes across to pick up a cassette player and begins to rummage through a drawer. He finds the tape he has been looking for.*)

ROBINS

Go on, girls. Sit yourselves down for amoment. Make yourselves at home.

(*He places cassette recorder on the desk, plugs it in and puts in a cassette. SAM and GINA look at one another ominously.*)

It's my birthday today. (*pause*) What? I didn't hear you girls.

SAM & GINA

Happy birthday Mr.Robins.

ROBINS

You know when I was small and it was my birthday my mum used to get some friends over from school. I must have been just six or seven. We used to play some games. Then we'd have a big tea, cake, jelly – Mum would always do me proud with a big cake, candles with my name written in icing on the top. It tended to be written in blue. That's quite a masculine colour, don't you think, girls? (*Pause*)

But you know what I really miss?

(*He turns to face them. They shake their heads.*)

The games. You know, pass the parcel, postman's knock, pin the tail on the donkey, blind man's bluff. But do you know which was my favourite?

SAM & GINA
No.

ROBINS
Musical chairs. You know, Mummy plays some music
and we all run round the chairs. And then one chair is
taken away and the music stops. The last one left standing
without a chair is out. So, let's have a practice run.

SAM
Mr.Robins, I just want my cheque. Then we've really got
to go.

ROBINS (*ignoring Sam, directly to Gina*)
I hear they've just made two hundred and fifty
redundant at the watch factory. Word is that they'll be
closed down completely by the end of the year.I thought
you were happy here, Gina.

GINA
I am Mr.Robins, but I've really got to go. My mum's
been looking after the kids. She needs to get into town.

ROBINS
Now, Gina, be reasonable. What's more important?
Mum getting into town a few minutes late or you being
able to bring home a decent wage for your family.
And all to please an old man on his birthday. Now, stand
up. Come on. Chop, chop.

(*He claps his hands together. He removes a revolver from his pocket and
places it on the table in front of the machine. He searches through his
pockets.*)

Where are the presents for my two girls? Here we go.

(*He removes two small parcels of white tissue paper and gives one to
SAM and the other to GINA.*)

Go on. Open them.

(The girls exchange glances and gingerly open the packages. They each contain a large chicken's comb made from bright red material with a piece of string attached to each side. ROBINS is eager to see their reaction.)

Put them on, put them on.

(Both girls place the objects on their heads and tie the string under their chin.)

We can use two chairs for the practice. Round and round you'll go. My two little chicks fighting for their perch. Now, lets see if we can cheep.

(Pause. The girls stare at him, shocked.)

Come on!

(They sense a change in his tone and reproduce feeble cheeping sounds.)

Louder!

(They cheep louder.)

We must do this properly. Arm movements as well. Come on, up and down. Flap those wings.

(The girls push their elbows out and self-consciously flap their 'wings' several times.)

Here we go for the first time.

(He turns on the tape and it plays the beginning of the 'Birdie Song' by The Tweets)

Come on girls, round we go.

(SAM and GINA circle the chairs flapping their arms. ROBINS stops the tape and the girls stop too, but just remain standing.)

Sit down!

(they sit)

Right. you remove one of the chairs, Gina. Put it against the wall.

(She complies with his directions. SAM remains seated.)

Here we go. It's for real this time.

(ROBINS starts the music again. They move self-consciously around the chairs flapping their arms as little as possible.)

Come on! Round we go.

(He stops the music after 10 to 15 seconds. The girls look at him and then each other.)

Come on. Which one is it? You're not playing properly. One of you. Sit!

(SAM indicates to GINA. GINA is reluctant to be the one to sit, but SAM stands firm. GINA lowers herself on to the chair.)

Oh, how gracious of you to be the first loser, Sam. We've got a special forfeit.

(He puts the gun down on the desk and begins to rummage in one of the desk drawers.)

Just while I remember.

(Before the girls have time to realize what is happening he opens the gun, slips in six bullets and snaps the chamber closed. He points the gun in front of him and turns to face SAM.)

That'd be no good at all, would it? Now, Sam, all I want you to do is to answer a question or two. Is that okay?

SAM
Yes.

ROBINS
What would you do if I asked you to work here for nothing?

SAM
I don't know.

ROBINS
You must know.

SAM
Well, of course I wouldn't.

(ROBINS cocking the revolver.)

ROBINS
What did you say?

(SAM is in tears and her response can hardly be heard through her sobbing.)

SAM
Yes.

ROBINS
Good. Good girl. So, why do you work here, Sam?

SAM *(through her tears.)*
I need the money.

ROBINS
And?

SAM
I badly need the money. I need it for the shopping. I just need the money to live.

(GINA puts her hand up to SAM's and squeezes it.)

ROBINS
Very good. Very good. Very satisfying. Let's go.
(He turns the music on again and raises his voice above the noise.)
And make sure you use those arms properly.

(The girls circle the chair. ROBINS turns the music off. The girls look at each other. GINA is staying put. SAM understands and sits down.)

How very egalitarian. So, tell me. Why do you work here, Gina?

GINA
The same as Sam. I need the money.

ROBINS
That's not quite what I mean, Gina. What sort of girl do you think works here, Gina?

GINA
Normal girl.

ROBINS
Normal?

GINA
Well, not trained.

ROBINS
What you mean is they're not capable of being trained? Not capable of better things? Bit simple?

GINA
No!

ROBINS
Didn't you work hard at school, Gina?

GINA
I didn't do too bad.

ROBINS
But, you're here.

GINA
Well, perhaps I didn't work hard enough.

ROBINS
Lot of girls who didn't work quite hard enough in your school, were there?

GINA
What do you mean?

ROBINS
We're talking about failures. Those who haven't made anything of their lives, Gina? Still we must look on the bright side. You've made it into our humble little coop here and you've got Colonel Rooster who will open his wing to you and let you nestle against his breast feathers – away from the nasties of the outside world.

(Pause. ROBINS gently strokes his gun. He turns on the music. The girls begin to walk around the chairs again, exchanging glances. He stops the music and GINA sits.)

Do you think I could get any sort of girl to work here, Sam?

SAM
No, I don't know

ROBINS
No? What makes you say that?

SAM
Well, obviously not every girl wants to work here.

(moving closer to SAM)

ROBINS
What would she be like, a girl who didn't want to work here?

SAM
I don't know. She'd probably talk all posh. She'd be properly educated.

ROBINS
Would she be pretty?

(puting his hand up to her face)

> **SAM**
> Yes, I expect she would.
>
> **ROBINS**
> And what would she wear?
>
> **SAM**
> She'd have nice clothes.
>
> **ROBINS**
> And what would she wear here?

(unbuttoning the top buttons of her blouse and stroking her neck gently with one finger)

> **SAM**
> Pearls. She'd have a string of pearls.
>
> **ROBINS**
> Mmmm. Nice. Two out of three says you're the loser, Sam. Get up onto the table. You're going to do a little dance for me all alone. Colonel Cockerel wants to see what his chicklet has hidden up her tail feathers. Up you

get.

(She clambers on top of the table. ROBINS turns the music on. She begins to dance. Flapping her arms up and down. She seems to be becoming slightly immune to the humiliation and stares off into the distance as she gets on with her chicken act.)

> **ROBINS**
> Faster, faster!

(He removes his shirt and tie. He stands up, straight and proud, Passing an open palm slowly down his chest to his flies which he starts unbuttoning.)

CUT TO MID SHOT OF DESK ON WHICH SAM IS DANCING
ROBINS approaches the table from the left, his gun still in his right hand. His trousers are slipping down his thighs and his pants are pulled

down revealing his buttocks. GINA remains seated to the right of the desk.

ROBINS
Why do you work here, Sam? Why?

(He begins to raise his arm and the gun, pointing between SAM's legs, begins to pull up her skirt. She grits her teeth, her eyes blaze through her tears as she stamps her foot down onto his dick resting on the table in front of her. The gun goes off and he squeals with pain.)

SAM
I don't work here.

(ROBINS rolls on the floor in agony, clutching his groin. SAM is furious and screams.)

Through accident of birth I may be uneducated, I may not talk proper, but my God I deserve as much as anyone.

(SAM jumps down from the table and takes GINA by the arm.)

Come on.

(GINA looks over her shoulder as they walk out of the office. Almost immediately SAM remembers the cheque and comes back in. ROBINS gropes for the gun. She walks over to the desk and retrieves the envelope. His hand finds the gun and he aims. She ducks as she exits, screaming out.)

SAM
Fuck you!

(The door slams shut and a bullet hits the frame. Sounds disappear off down the corridor. ROBINS moans, gets to his feet and heads over to the minibar beside his desk. With one hand still clutching his groin he opens a bottle of champagne and pours it over his dick. Wincing with pain he sings in a psychotic manner.)

ROBINS
Happy birthday . . . to me, happy . . . birthday to me. Happy birthday . . . dear Colonel Rooster . . . happy . . . .

FADE OUT.

Indian Summer

Matthew McGuchan

Matthew McGuchan began his career by studying fine art at St Martin's College. He has made two short films *The Enchanted Forest* (1993), *Isle of Dogs* (1996), with funding from the British Film Institute and BBC 2. He lives and works in London.

1. EXT. BOARDED-UP COTTAGE. MORNING. A cottage nestles in the heart of a wood, enveloped by flowers and bird-song. Setting and score suggest the Victorian era. PULL FOCUS TO FOREGROUND and cut to ANIMATION: the foliage rustles with life as a number of small, strange, dark, winged figures crawl from under leaf and shadow to peer at the cottage.

INT. COTTAGE. SLOW TRACK THROUGH SHADOWY CLUTTERED INTERIOR. The walls are lined with overflowing shelves containing books, jars, bundles of wires. We can hear the sound of an OLD MAN's voice, muttering to himself.

TRACK ALONG MANTELPIECE. A daguerreotype of a woman's face, a clock, a snow-globe paperweight.

TRACK ACROSS DESK. Wires, cogs, photographic equipment. Plans spread out over the desk, plans for an elaborate contraption. A small winged figure, sketched-in at the mouth of the contraption. A gnarled finger runs across the plans.

> *OLD MAN'S VOICE*
> We'll see – we'll just see who wins . . .

EXT. COTTAGE. POINT-OF-VIEW SHOT, looking through a gap in the window-boards into the cottage. The OLD MAN works at his desk, fiddling with mechanical bits and pieces.

CLOSE-UP OF A YOUNG GIRL, dressed in Victorian style, peering through the gap in the boards, her head just above the sill.

INT. COTTAGE. Gnarled fingers pour powder from a leather pouch into a metal dish. The OLD MAN's eyes glitter, following the wires that run from the powder-tray to a Leyden jar, and from there to a box-camera.

EXT. COTTAGE. The GIRL stands on a YOUNG BOY's back.

>**GIRL**
>[*Whispering*] Higher . . . !

The BOY grunts. The GIRL edges closer.

INT. COTTAGE. The OLD MAN tests the tension of a cable that runs from the box-camera. When the cable is pulled, the camera shutter opens. The OLD MAN smiles, connects up the Leyden jar to the rest of the equipment. He takes the end of the cable in his hand and, averting his face, pulls hard upon it.

EXT. COTTAGE. An explosion, a flash of light from inside the cottage. The GIRL falls backwards over the BOY, letting out a yelp of surprise.

There is the clatter and clunk of heavy locks being undone. The GIRL rubs her eyes, looks up. The OLD MAN stands on the porch, soot-blackened, looking angry. A wisp of smoke drifts from the opened door. We see his face clearly for the first time – he is extremely old.

>**OLD MAN**
>Clear off, do you hear me?

The OLD MAN swings his cane at the children, who run away, shrieking. The OLD MAN brushes down his long velvet jacket, looks round anxiously, and steps back inside the cottage.

2. EXT. WOOD. DAY. The GIRL and the BOY hide behind a bush, watching from a distance as the OLD MAN rigs up his equipment. The box-camera stands on a tripod, the Leyden jar is tucked behind a tree. The OLD MAN descends a ladder. We can see various bits of apparatus poking out from beneath foliage.

A cable runs from the jar along the bough of a tree to where the OLD MAN stands. CLOSE-UP OF OLD MAN, as he suspends a locket from the end of the concealed cable. The locket contains a daguerreotype of a woman's face.

In the distance we can see the CHILDREN watching through parted foliage. CHILDREN'S POINT-OF-VIEW: the OLD MAN shoots suspicious glances about himself as he hobbles into hiding behind a nearby bush. The CHILDREN creep closer.

CLOSE-UP OF OLD MAN, settling on a tree-stump, staring intently at the trap he has set.

CLOSE-UP OF SILVER LOCKET, turning slowly in the breeze.

The CHILDREN crouch nearby, contemplating the glittering trinket. The GIRL leans over to the BOY, whispers in his ear. The boy nods, dives under the nearest bush.

MID-SHOT OF OLD MAN, who sits and concentrates on the scene. All is quiet. The OLD MAN yawns.

MID-SHOT OF BOY, crawling through the undergrowth.

CLOSE-UP OF GIRL, her gaze caught by the gently-twisting locket. She does not notice the powder-tray that sits on the ground in front of her, the wires and rods that protrude from the foliage above. The box-camera towers in front of her, covering the scene with its blind eye.

The BOY flattens himself out against a tree trunk. A few yards away the OLD MAN can be seen, staring with heavy lids into the distance. The BOY hefts a lump of dead wood in his hand.

CLOSE-UP OF OLD MAN'S EYES, as they flutter and close.

DREAM VISION. PIXILATION: a gazebo, somewhere in the heart of the wood. A vision of peace, framed by butterflies and flowering roses. A bent, aged figure, toiling up a slope towards the small wooden building.

EXT. WOOD. A lump of wood strikes the OLD MAN on the side of the head.

> **OLD MAN**
> What the devil . . . !?

SLOW-MOTION: The GIRL jumps from cover and grabs the locket.

The camera shutter snaps open.

THE MAGNESIUM POWDERS EXPLODE IN A BLAZE OF LIGHT. As they do so, a cage contraption drops from the cover of leaves towards the girl, knocking her to the ground. The BOY gasps, horrified.

The OLD MAN scuttles over to his equipment. Waving the smoke away with a hand, he examines the dangling fragment of cable, inspects the trap. It is empty. He seems puzzled, then looks up as the BOY darts past him.

The GIRL lies on the ground, unconscious. The BOY is beside her, stuffing something in his pocket. THE OLD MAN comes up behind him.

> **OLD MAN**
> What is it? What have you found?
>
> **BOY**
> My sister . . .

The GIRL lets out a low moan.

> **OLD MAN**
> [*His eyes narrow with suspicion*] Were you up to something, the pair of you?
>
> **BOY**
> [*Anxious*] No, sir, honestly. We were just playing.
>
> **OLD MAN**
> Hmm . . .

The GIRL moans again, louder. The OLD MAN grimaces, looks up at the darkening sky.

> **OLD MAN**
> Come on. Back to the cottage.

3. EXT. COTTAGE. LATE AFTERNOON. The OLD MAN hurries along the path towards the cottage, the GIRL over his shoulder. The BOY follows behind, staggering under the weight of the box-camera. Night is setting in, and with it, winter. ANIMATION: leaves curl up and fall from the branches that frame the scene.

MID-SHOT OF COTTAGE DOOR. The OLD MAN produces a huge bunch of keys, addresses the many locks of the cottage door.

> **OLD MAN**
> You can never be too careful...

4. INT. COTTAGE "DARK ROOM". Aged hands light a candle, cover it with red glass.

The OLD MAN eagerly unscrews the back of the box-camera.

> **OLD MAN**
> Now then – let us see . . .

5. INT. COTTAGE MAIN ROOM. The BOY sits wrapped-up in a blanket, in front of a blazing fire. The GIRL slumps in an armchair, her eyes closed, murmuring feverishly. BOY'S POINT-OF-VIEW, scanning the mantelpiece above the fire: the clock, the snow-globe paperweight, the daguerreotype portrait in its pewter frame.

The BOY takes the locket from his pocket – it holds the same portrait as the one on the mantelpiece. He puts the locket away, turns his gaze to the fire. In the background the GIRL quivers.

CLOSE-UP OF THE GIRL'S HAIR. ANIMATION: tiny cogs and watch-parts wheel from her tresses, dispersing across the back of the armchair . . .

INT. "DARK ROOM". The OLD MAN shuffles and mutters, vague movement in the red-tinted darkness. There is the clink of glass and the slosh of liquid.

INT. MAIN ROOM. ANIMATION: a cog wheels across the OLD MAN'S opened notebook. Another climbs the length of a candle, quaking in the heat of the flame. Still another rolls across the skin of the BOY'S forearm, leaving a trail of pin-pricks that seep trembling droplets of blood. PIXILATION: the BOY gasps.

ANIMATION: the watch-parts have congregated on the mantelpiece, surrounding the snow-globe paperweight.

PIXILATION: the GIRL opens her eyes.

INT. "DARK ROOM". The cover is removed from the candle. The OLD MAN raises the still-wet calotype to the light, and his eyes widen with alarm.

CLOSE-UP OF CALOTYPE: the GIRL'S flash-blinded face, her hand grasping the locket. Around her head a swarm of small, strange, dark, winged, motion-blurred figures . . .

INT. MAIN ROOM. PIXILATION: The GIRL stands in front of the snow-globe. Slowly she reaches out, places her hands upon it.

> **OLD MAN** *[off-screen]*
> Don't you dare . . . !

PIXILATION: the OLD MAN'S cane strikes the GIRL'S arm. THE ARM SNAPS OFF AT THE ELBOW AND FALLS TO THE FLOOR.

The OLD MAN backs away from the GIRL, holding his cane out in front of himself.

ANIMATION: the GIRL'S arm lies on the floor in a mess of broken glass and clock-parts. It is hollow, made of porcelain. A number of tiny cogs scurry out-of-sight into it.

The GIRL turns to face the OLD MAN.

> **GIRL**
> Sebastopol has fallen. Father will be home soon.

The OLD MAN brings the cane down again and again, eyes wide

with horror. The room echoes with the sound of breaking china.

There is a whimper from behind the armchair. The OLD MAN gasps for breath, looks up. The BOY cowers in the shadows, a pair of eyes wrapped in a blanket.

The OLD MAN crouches next to the boy, prods his cheek. The skin depresses like normal flesh. The OLD MAN grunts, squints.

> *BOY*
> My sister . . .

> *OLD MAN*
> Trust me boy, that was not your sister. [*He looks up*] She must still be out there – with them.

CLOSE-UP OF WINDOW. Through the cracks in the boards, we can see snow flurrying.

6. INT. COTTAGE. LATER. The BOY sits in the armchair, his hands around a steaming cup. He looks distraught. The OLD MAN wraps a great cloak about himself, turns to face the BOY.

> *OLD MAN*
> The faeries are after my soul, boy. But I have hidden it from them. Somewhere in this room, they are right about that.

The OLD MAN shoots a glance at the snow-globe before settling his gaze on the daguerreotype of a woman's serene face.

> *OLD MAN*
> It was my lack of vigilance that allowed them to steal my beloved Mary from me, but I will not be fooled again. I shall announce my return with three distinct knocks upon the door. Let no one else in, no matter whom, or indeed, what they might appear to be. Do you hear? [*The BOY nods*] I shall be back shortly, God willing.

The BOY watches fearfully as the old man leaves.

7. EXT. WOOD. NIGHT. The OLD MAN walks through the wood. He holds a hurricane lamp aloft, his shoulders set against wind and snow. In the flickering light he looks fearfully around.

>*OLD MAN*
>Child? Child, where are you!

The OLD MAN wipes his brow, looking round at the tangle of rose-bushes and rhododendrons.

>*OLD MAN*
>I swear the path has changed . . .

8. INT. COTTAGE. NIGHT. The BOY sits in the armchair, half-asleep. The fire crackles, dying down.

There is a tapping at the window. The BOY stirs, looks round.

>*GHOSTLY VOICE*
>Brother . . .

The BOY gets up, walks cautiously over to the window.

>*GHOSTLY VOICE*
>Brother, it's me . . .

The BOY opens the window, struggling with the boards that cover it, and leans out. The wind swoops.

EXT. WOOD. NIGHT. The OLD MAN wanders through a wood that seems without end.

>*OLD MAN*
>Child? Child? Are you there?

The OLD MAN stumbles into the darkness, pulling his cloak around himself. The feeble light of his lamp is gradually lost amongst the dark mass of trees and foliage.

BLACK SCREEN. The sound of bird-song.

9. EXT. WOOD. MORNING. The OLD MAN opens his eyes and looks round with growing astonishment.
Summer has returned to the garden. Flowers are in bloom, birds are singing. The OLD MAN emerges from his sheltering-place in a bowl of roots, blinking.

>*OLD MAN*
>Remarkable . . . !

Through the bushes the OLD MAN catches sight of the BOY, who stands looking out into the wood. He marches over to him.

>*OLD MAN*
>I told you not to leave the cottage, stupid child!

>*BOY*
>She's coming. Look . . .

PIXILATION: a small figure approaches them through the trees. Her presence is vague, ethereal.

>*OLD MAN*
>Girl? Is that you?

PIXILATION: as the GIRL nears us we can discern a myriad gossamer-winged figures clinging to her dress, trembling in the breeze.

Tears form in the OLD MAN'S eyes. The GIRL raises her arms.

ANIMATION: A SWARM OF FAERIES FLY FROM THE GIRL'S BODY TOWARDS THE OLD MAN.

PIXILATION: the OLD MAN cowers, batting blindly at the air as the swarm flies past him towards the BOY. He turns to see the BOY holding out an object towards the faeries. It is the SNOW-GLOBE PAPERWEIGHT from the OLD MAN's mantelpiece..!

>*OLD MAN*
>NO . . . !

PIXILATION: the OLD MAN lashes out at the BOY with his cane, knocking him to the ground. ANIMATION: the BOY'S form collapses, leaving only a garment stuffed with twigs and leaves, from which a single spider crawls.

PIXILATION: the OLD MAN grabs the fallen ornament, swiping at the faeries that swarm around it, and runs off into the wood.

10. EXT. WOOD. DUSK. PIXILATION: The OLD MAN stumbles through the gloom, crying out at every unexpected branch that blocks his way.

11. EXT. BANK OF STREAM. DUSK. PIXILATION: The OLD MAN staggers to a halt at the edge of a stream, gasping ragged breaths of air. He limps forward to the water's edge, takes a tentative step into the flow. It reaches only to his ankles. He takes another step forward – a little deeper, but manageable.

REVERSE WIDE SHOT OF SCENE. PIXILATION: with painful slowness the OLD MAN fords the stream. PULL OUT TO REVEAL GAZEBO, nestling by a stand of trees on the further bank.
The OLD MAN's brow furrows with vague recognition. Light wanes from the grey wall of the sky.

12. INT. GAZEBO. DUSK. The OLD MAN settles himself with a sigh on the bench inside the Gazebo. He pulls his cloak around himself, investigates the weight in his pocket and withdraws the forgotten ornament. Light glistens through the crystalline dome as he inspects the scene it contains – a gazebo, with the forest looming behind.

The OLD MAN'S eyes lift slowly upwards. The BOY stands in front of him, wrapped in modern-day winter clothes. The GIRL waits at the entrance. Their faces show concern and puzzlement.

SLOW-MOTION: the OLD MAN'S eyes flutter and close.

The BOY gently pries the OLD MAN'S fingers from the snowglobe. He holds it up to the light. The GIRL watches over his shoulder.

With a shake of the BOY'S hand, winter begins.

DISSOLVE TO WIDE SHOT OF SCENE, AS SNOW BEGINS TO FALL.

Her Story.
History.

Sue Powell

Susan Powell was born in Wales and lives in Hertfordshire. She writes short stories and verse and has begun a play for radio. She is currently working on two novels, one of them based on the piece in this anthology.

Healing cells around a wound, we women gather at the gates, guarding the perimeter of life.

An inscrutable winter's day, the new year imminent. Sparse time of grey light, when outer life shuts down. Our visitors have gone – they brought us food, clothes, wood for our fire. We huddle around the flames, eat a scant meal, talk, sing, make up stories and contemplate the gathering tangibility of night. We move nearer the fire, nearer each other and our thoughts turn inward.

They come from the town to scourge and revile us, cast filth upon us, excrement, blood. We do not claim to be extraordinary, though some say garlanded like saints. Beyond the wire, soldiers shout abuse with mouths that grope for absent sex. Night engulfs us and fears invade this no man's land. Over the perimeter wire we have woven a web. Damp soaks it but wetness under the remorseless lights makes the coloured threads miraculous.

Our bodies become the mud they imitate and we seek another way than war. The parameters of selfhood are not drawn by assaults upon others. Our presence and our speech persuade. Compassion, though it opens wounds, defeats force.

These missiles threaten all futures - the shining weaponry, no armour but a shaft that destroys. Useless, the fenced fear, the fixed points and cold pricks, poised to shoot. These weapons lurking beneath the silos aim at the end of the world.

We do not number our days with hours but with convictions and no longer bear the scars of conformity. We are happier as targets of abuse than thirty pieces of cruising silver.

The moon is smeared by war. Since that sin, the world is seen through the lens of destruction. Trees, flowers, are still calendars, unseen by those who, marring vision with complacency, fear with blood, see only through the inferno.

We are an organism.

My own life, Greenham, one year now.

December 1982 and my first national demonstration. So many women. Women only. The coach was a hive of talk, song, laughter. One or two sat with an empty seat beside them, contemplative, looking out of the window but the fifty-seater was almost full. Maggie and I talked, read our briefing notes.

"If I get arrested, make sure you tell Bob!"

"You won't get arrested. You're not going to do anything illegal."

"You never know."

"Do you think there'll really be enough of us to link arms around the whole base? It's nine miles."

"Well they say it will just happen. They don't like the idea of leaders."

"They?"

"The women."

We arrived and a humming stream poured out, multi-colouring the grey tarmac in small crowds – blue, red, green, violet, turquoise, indigo and orange. Then we saw the base. The fence contained an interminable expanse of grey concrete, the grass and scrub of common land, incarcerated in grey, grey, grey. In the near distance, women were decorating the fence, filling the steel-bound spaces, weaving. Webs of wool, pictures, photographs of children and people smiling, drawings of flowers, endowing the implacable metal with warmth, colour and irreplacable moments in a history of love. There were no casual offerings on the wire: ribbons, a baby's mitten or tiny woollen boot.

We walked around the fence, passing hundreds of women: sweaters, woolly hats, baggy trousers, long skirts, scarves – a multiplicity of clothes and colours and the busyness of ants, bodies wavering in and out of kilter as two lines moved in opposite directions, both hugging the perimeter. Slipping on the mud, helping each other up, greeting, laughing, pausing to take in the scene on both sides of the wire.

Something happened then. Movement slowed, women began to stand still, to turn and take hands. Chains of arms formed, hands linking, embracing the base, we stretched, a line of women from here to invisibility. Singing began to swell, humming, shouts and joy spilling over as a force like healing passed through our hands laid on. The strongest moment of my life so far and I had no name for it.

Dark was imminent as we set off three hours later, back to the meeting point for the coaches. Small groups lingered round fires or circles of bobbing candlelight. I knew that amongst those who stayed, were the women who kept daily vigil while we got on with our lives. They sat or crouched near the flames and orange light touched their features. We said little, exhilarated but feeling guilt seep in with the night's damp. We trudged back with the perimeter fence always in view on our right, hostile and sombre: I was glad Maggie was with me. My boots were starting to rub up a blister, which hurt with every step.

We nearly missed the coach. Searching for it down the lines of smoke-bellowing vehicles, we coughed at fumes that blurred the clear air. At the front of the line, a makeshift roll-call was taking place. As each coach came up, someone called out its group and destination. "Chester CND. Cambridge Women's Group. Northern Quakers. . . " Ours arrived just as we got to the front of the line. We climbed on board hurriedly – the last two.

"God knows what we'd have done if we'd missed it."

"It's a long walk to Norwich. Any food left?"

Most of the women on the coach seemed buoyant, inspired. I chewed the last of the sandwiches and looked out of the grubby window at the spray, the wet road and the wavering trails of red and white car lights.

Before going to bed, I wandered into my study and turned on the desk lamp. There was my manuscript, typed with my alterations in tiny scribblings in the margins. Words of war and my characters' names standing out on the page: Michael, Jacob. I felt a mother's fondness for them in the wash of warm light that encircled the sheets.

*

The harvest was early that year. There was no breeze over the meadow and even the sky was still; ears of corn stood, close-packed and alert, while the sky fermented through the deep haze. There was a path broken between the corn and larks soared. A young man lay with his head in his sister's lap, eyes

141

closed. Hers were fixed on his face.

"We must go, Michael. Mother's had Jamie all afternoon. Michael . . . "

She stirred her legs slightly and he opened his eyes, squinting at the sudden light.

"Is it late?"

"Look at the shadows."

"Come on then."

As they brushed through the tall crop, he glanced across at Sarah, seeing how the untied wisps of his sister's hair wandered across her cheek.

Shots rang out far beyond their Gloucestershire hills: in the significant distance, marking an end to peace. They met her child hurrying to meet them.

"I've waited ever so long. Carry me, Uncle."

At the house, the door was low and Michael had to bend well below the rough beam to bring the boy on his shoulders safely into the kitchen. That day elsewhere, war began.

An office was set up in their town and men and boys jostled to enlist. There was a tremulousness at the borders that, swollen, filled the air. Michael went too, though against his sister's wishes. She had lost one man already, to the farm, was not deceived, could see the end of his going and sought to hold him before he fell, diverted into the rhythm of violence.

The exuberance was unchecked. Michael noticed boys manifestly below enlistment age. Some had attempted a scratching of a beard. Others, honest, were sent away.

"How old are you, son?"

"Sixteen, sir."

The sergeant leaned over, grossly avuncular, man-to-man, with a huge conspiratorial wink. "Well come back tomorrow, when you're nineteen."

Touching the ripe seductions of a man's world, it seemed that into battle they escaped.

*

On the Saturday after our Greenham trip I went into Norwich to get some Christmas shopping. Jarrolds was bright with white lights, tiered like a wedding cake. Joining the crush, I was swept past a syrupy, American voice crooning *White Christmas* and *Silent Night*. Squeaking children piled in on the chorus. The old busker was outside Smith's, waving his woollen mitten with a face stitched on it and, with the other hand, bouncing his string puppet up and down to *Rudolph the Red-Nosed Reindeer* crackling from his cassette player. That was all he ever did to invite the money of passing shoppers. This Saturday he wore a Santa hat.

Windows were draped with wreaths, plastic holly and swathes of synthetic foliage over mirrors: Christmas, doubly artificial in reflection; over-red berries and brash posters whose imperative was a fusion of Christmas spirit with spend, spend, spend. People shopped as if at war, other shoppers, the enemy. I had a gloomy sense of the excess of it all: the vicious spiral of consumersim snagged up on genuine longings for goodwill. I felt an ascetic recoil, nun-like and thought of the Greenham women. As I walked away from the square, one of the drinkers who gather on the benches near C&A stood up, leaned forward and vomited copiously on the pavement.

I packed a case and came here to Greenham on Christmas Eve: clothes, sleeping bag, a few books, a torch, my manuscript. I could feel its tiny lineaments stir, as I carried it like a child.

Faces. Firelight. All else an absolute cold. Our silence a Christmas.

*

Conditions in the train were cramped. Tommies stood, sat, or huddled on kitbags. The few seats were over-full. Night came and Michael saw his companions with difficulty. At times a passing light would discover their faces. Occasionally, someone would strike a match, light a cigarette. Such gestures modified the dark. They knew little of each other but there was an ellipse of intensity, awareness, that joined them, a fascination none quite acknowledged: a bond of half-light and of flux. When they pulled into the station, there was mud on the carriage floor that confused the shine.

"This way!"

He turned from Michael, who followed silently. The trench was two feet wide and deep as a man. Down it flowed the familiar mud. Every time he stepped forward, his foot sank in and sludge welled up towards his thighs. Once, he clean lost a boot as mud slid in. Gradually it became easier going and Michael caught his first glimpse of Keeley and Sim, buttocks towards him. They were leaning up over a shallow trench wall, resting on a line of sandbags, using a periscope to observe the enemy lines.

Above the men, jutting out black and crippled where the skyline broke, were the crossed remains of charred trees, trunks and branches: burnt, angular, like thorns and broken limbs.

"*Christ, that's a bloody ugly view.*" *Hearing him, they turned and laughed, thinking he meant them.*

*

The taxi dropped me off at Main Gate. I stood for a while with my suitcase beside me and the straps of my rucksack cutting into my shoulder. I seemed to stand an inordinate time looking at the circle of tousled women who wore a jumble sale of clothes. They looked at me once or twice. I stood for several minutes feeling foolish and self-conscious, wishing I hadn't come.

One of the women got up – cropped hair, heavy boots. Walking over, she glanced at my suitcase and, with a light smile, said, "have you come to stay?"

We both looked at my luggage and laughed.

For the first few days I had some space in the ambulance. Then they showed me how to build a bender, using branches and sheets of plastic. I share it with Kath.

My suitcase is a storage box in the ambulance. My clothes have augmented the general stock: Liz is wearing my big green jumper, Chris has two pairs of my thick tights on and, wearing the woolly hat that Gran knitted for me, Josie is giving an innovative angle to millinery at Greenham this winter.

Yesterday when I looked across at the soldier behind the wire he called out, ". . . new one aren't you nice long hair not like the others love to get my hands on you rub that hair of yours over my cock feel those tits of yours hand on your cunt like to fuck you . . ."

Today, like the others, I sit with my back to the base. I hold a mug of hot tea. It warms my hands and the steam rises, making my nose run. I focus on the hot tea smell and try to forget the shock of his aggression.

This morning, a pile of old dry leaves had shored up at the entrance to the bender, a scratching of dry brown against the milky plastic, gradually made sodden and voiceless by the heavy dew.

At the next gate, the women have made a garden: circles of small stones; a shell; flushed leaves and the shine of acorns made into a web. They tell us that every day they decorate the fence with coloured wool, darning the gaps, softening the metal. They hang pictures they've drawn and peace messages. Most days the soldiers tear them down. Small determinations: wider purposes.

I tore off the last blank page of my manuscript today and wrote my own message to put on the fence near the gate.

*

That winter, a boy joined them. Even later, Michael never knew why such a disbeliever should seek the front line. Jacob, they called him. At first there was a slight leaving, a detaching of themselves from him: he prompted troubling thoughts. Why should they recall things missing from the darkness? Much later, they understood how he could fill the dread spaces their women abandoned them to and they mothered him. He summoned the part of their lives that was still humane.

Unsure why, Michael observed the boy closely, on days when routine tasks brought them together. His eyes were vivid green and, glancing up, ingenuous, apprehensive. Also vehemently alive. His cheeks were so smooth that Michael wondered how he had been admitted until he recalled the day of his own enlistment.

The face was evenly curved, the brows dark and close, emphasizing the questioning lines on the forehead. His mouth was almost too vulnerable and the lips broad, softened above by a downy shadow. Jacob would raise his eyes quizzically, then, aware of the older man's recoil from their frankness, would dip his head as if from a slight cuff. When he spoke, which was rare, it was with the soft tones of the West Country.

*

Our feet have become unused to stepping on concrete – turf, leaves, grass, treading the ripe mould that softens the woods is like a dance – the sharp pungency of fallen and fermenting leaves – a kind of sweet wine. Our time is measured in the fall of water drops from branches, cycles of light from cold darkness to cold day. I have never felt cold as I feel it here. The parameters of flesh and blood are frost clear.

A week after joining the camp I went into the woods, foraging for kindling. It was early, chill January with a mist that fluctuated over branches and crystallised spiders' webs. I suddenly came across Josie. She was just inside the wood, crouching by one of the plastic water containers, an old bowl in front of her. She knelt over it and, scooping up the water in cupped hands, drenched her face, rubbed then drenched again, passing liquid fingers over eyes, nose, mouth. She shook her head vigorously. Water drops shot through the light and scattered to the ground. With swift, smooth strokes, she washed ears, neck and throat, sinuous as a cat, then picked up a small towel to wipe herself dry.

I paused, an unwilling intruder. Josie whipped up her jumper and shirt and tugged them over her head. She knelt down, naked to the waist, flexed her brown arms and stretched her shoulder muscles. Her upper body was pale as the inside of a shell. I watched the skin move over the muscles as they stretched and loosened and saw how in the sharp morning light, the left shoulder blade cut a deep shadow to her waist. I felt sudden tenderness for her open body and shivered at the early cold.

She took soap, lathered up her brown hands, rubbed suds over her body, arms, shoulders; under arms and slipping down over breasts that sharpened in the chill air. Leaning on one arm, she made an arc over the bowl and her breasts swayed as she splashed off the lather. Water trickled down over her body, was caught before she splashed again, changed arms and repeated the movements as if in reflection. She sat up and rubbed herself vigorously with the towel, chasing up a flush of red on her pale skin, while I, an accidental voyeur, felt more and more awkward but reluctant to leave.

It felt irreverent to stay and now, dishonest to go.

After pulling on her clothes, she turned and was momentarily startled to see me. She tipped out the water and shook the bowl. Collecting the water-carrier, she walked over.

"I didn't . . . I wouldn't have come this way if I'd known," I said. "Isn't this a bit Spartan? You must be freezing."

"More like a luxury: water's scarce here. But I'm collecting a new load at nine."

We talked as we strolled back to the camp, her arm lightly around my waist.

We had visitors this afternoon. Three girls and a woman: schoolgirls and their teacher. They were tentative, discreet and sat some distance away at first and only came over when invited.

They had a mug of tea with us, while we answered their questions, told them something of our life here. They were cautious, though, not quite sure where the mugs had been. The teacher in particular, took tight little sips, her lips hardly touching the edge of the mug.

At about three, while they are still with us, there is some activity at the gate. A coach pulls out. As it swings round and turns down the road, we are greeted with a perfectly rehearsed manouevre. A dozen military arses – ten white and two black – are rammed against the steamy panes of the bus. The colours of hatred. I watch the girls' faces, sorry they are shocked but now they know more about how things are here.

"Giving us the evil eye," says Liz, running a hand through her ginger crop, and slinging the rest of her tea away behind us.

Round the fire as the light goes, we talk about our families. Jude cries. Her children are at home with their father. He seems to understand but they don't: they're only two and four. It has become too painful to see them every few weeks, she says. She can't stop crying today. Kate hugs her, strokes her hair, rocks her gently. There is nothing we can say.

*

Why seek the living among the dead? thought Michael. At night, bloated maggots fall gorging onto the sleepers from the corpsed mud of our dugout. Sleep in this earthen coffin? All we know are a few fitful hours of interminable waking, fragments of dreams.

They roused Michael suddenly from his half-sleep and within minutes, he was in battle gear. Where was Jacob in all this? Somewhere down the line. They stood in the dark, breath frosting the cobalt air, stamping their feet and rubbing their sparsely gloved hands, strung by the imminent prospect of attack. Where the narrow trench allowed, soldiers huddled together in threes and fours.

In time, word went along. Silent men gathered their gear and took up positions below the fire step. Michael waited, thought again of Jacob, then intently watched the framed sky. At a word, they clambered awkwardly over the parapet, rose and walked erect into the dark.

Instantly the shelling and clatter of guns broke out: he knew.

Figures shuddered over No Man's Land in the thronging light of blast after lurid blast. Noises rushed on the brain, exploding: the thud of shells and ruptured bodies; audible carnage. Michael saw Keeley take a German from the rear. With a huge, skyward arc of the rifle, he thrust his bayonet up through the spine, into the soft organs beyond, one, two, three. Blood sluiced out, summoned by his weapon. Michael pushed on, his feet gathering clay

147

while the earth split. He found himself suddenly on wire snagging his legs: an exploding shell punched him and he fell.

Into the night, memories moved through the intricacies of the past like breath into lungs. A dry whispering as if dead throats spoke. Pooled between clods of earth, was water that galvanized the pale sky. The near-ground groaned. Michael saw lumpish forms bob and sway on a mesh of barbed strands that flickered in the moonlight. On the wire were bodies of men shifting on the undertow of a dark tide, netted on a night sea. He turned home. . .

A serious child of four, staring into the fire, his face stinging, the musky smell of his sister's skirt as he clung to her. Logs cracked and spat. The child flinched. Michael slipped into the warm intercessing dark, the vulnerability of the receiving earth.

The young nurse moved to him across the ward. Lamplight deepened the places where compassion hid. Her voice came to him like slow hands through water. The scent of her was displaced and her sudden movement shocked him as she drew back the dressing from his wound.

*

Most of this morning was like a murky and sullen dawn. Daylight never really came. Earth and sky, one grey-brown wash in aggressive strokes. I had to keep my manuscript in my pocket all day: they tried to take everything except our clothes.

They've wiped out the camp.

The bailiffs came this morning. They pulled down the benders, took the boxes we sit on, the water containers and flung them on to the growing pile. Plates, mugs, saucepans, sleeping-bags, blankets, all committed to destruction. They pulled things from our hands; one of them knocked Kate's glasses off and left her fumbling on the ground. Liz picked them up, put them on her nose again, stroked her down. Jude was flapping like a lapwing near her nest - one of the men was tearing up her photographs and dropping the pieces in the mud. She cried as she tried to gather the pieces of her dismembered family.

The diggers moved in next and as the massive machines swung into position, their great arms lurching and dropping, we lay down in front of them but police pulled us out of the way. We kept moving in front, being pulled back, moving in front, being dragged away. We shouted up to the drivers about their families, about their children, that nuclear war would destroy. One of them told us to piss off to our own families, lowered the shovel and drove it straight through the camp. When he'd finished, there was just a space strewn with debris: mangled plastic sheets, ripped branches, crushed pots – a completely flattened kettle.

Since it happened this morning we've done nothing, said little. But we're staying.

Half two and a car pulls up. A man and a woman get out, middle-aged, well-dressed. They look at the desolation for a few moments. Children scramble out. The four of them begin to unpack things from the car. Another car pulls up, then another. Friends from Newbury.

They bring us firewood, water carriers, boxes of food, bread, coffee. The children struggle with their load.

"Heard about it on the radio," says Josh. We make a list – eggs, rice, salt, flour, toothpaste, Brillo pads, washing-up liquid.

While they're away getting the supplies, two young men pull up and stand near their car with rolls of plastic, a bag of potatoes. They stand some time in the car's shadow, unsure of the etiquette here. What do we mean by women only? They come over to us cautiously. One holds towards me a box of fire lighters. His breath is warm on my face as I hug him.

We begin again.

*

After they invalided him home, Michael spent his time helping a little around the farm, desultorily. Sarah noticed a monotone had entered his voice. He haunted the woods, the fields, but they seemed sullen under a brooding sky. They did not line up. He became introspective, moody. There were rows over nothing at all and to significant things he seemed not to respond. Home was an unsatisfactory peace. His thoughts turned with fondness to his men. To Jacob.

There was one terrible afternoon when for a reason he could not remember, he struck his little nephew. Sarah tried to comfort them both but his soul contained a breach that was irreparable.

Soon after, he went back to the war.

His sister was in the outhouse milking when he left. Moisture condensed on the small windows. She was squat at her stool, her hair loosely gathered that he had seen free and her head pushed firmly into the cow's flank. She took the udder and milked out the last warm drops, a taste he remembered. Rising, she turned to ease him of farewells. When he came to her embrace, the dusk was scented. Behind them the night gathered and down the misted pane waterdrops moved, tracing a dozen wandering trenches of lost tears.

The summer gave them a brief reprieve as they rested behind the lines. Yet Michael was uneasy at a need he could not name. He found Jacob often near him but feared his touch.

There were days when you could pretend, in the detached Flanders countryside, when with a radical shift of the imagination, you could shelve the war, set it aside. Days when they sat among tall grasses, insects buzzing past their ears: luxuriant days when they lay watching larks climb invisible bars in the air as their music ascended. On such days they clung to the heat like salvation.

At the old house that became their billet, Michael noticed an intensifying of the boy's presence. A third time, they almost touched but Michael moved away.

The grounds of the house were extensive and at some distance, amongst the reeds, Michael found the pool waiting. He tried to forget the boy's tremulousness but even here he heard the front line exploding and saw Jacob's face. He stripped and waded in. Michael felt the water reach shockingly cool over his thighs. His arms moved a slow, wide arc, and his legs spread in strong movement. He dived, a slow thrust against a conceding muscle of water and surfaced, splashing, into the light.

Day by day their ration seeped out, as the corner of autumn turned. Leaves already came incessantly, unobtrusively and slowly occupied the surface.

*

Kath must have woken first. I surfaced from light dreams to feel her finger pressed to my mouth. She was making very quiet 'Sh' sounds. We heard a rustle, a twig snap and as someone came closer to the bender, a proximity of hissing sibilants. There was a rush and a tip of something on top of us – heavy, fluid, it was pressing the roof down and cracking the branches. We shoved it back and something slithered down the outside. Again. A third time. Floundering about, we screamed and shoved at the sides of the shelter to push it off. Running feet, stumbling into the distance. Silence. The others' voices. Torch beams flashed through the plastic and away. I felt a sourness in my throat and thought I might be sick. Josie's voice: "Are you two okay in there?"

Then Liz, "God! Look at this stuff. Look what they've done."

"Shall we come out?"

They didn't answer.

We crawled out and stood up. All over the broken bender, were clots and pools of red-brown slurry. It ran down the folds and gathered on the grass, stinking. A disgusting mix of blood and shit. Bucketloads of it.

"It was maggots last time," said Jan. We stood in silence for some minutes. Liz put an arm round my shoulders and Josie was hugging Kath. Abruptly the chill reached us. I couldn't stop shivering.

"You'd better come into ours for the rest of the night. Bit of a squash but warm."

In the morning we had to drag the evil smelling slurry away on the plastic and dump it in the wood. We buried it under a pile of earth and leaves and did our best to clean down the sheeting with water.

I had to throw away my satchel and tear off the top page of my manuscript: blood had seeped in through the edge of the shelter and covered the writing.

Three thirty. Dark begins already. And now the winter takes hold in the seeping damp that occupies all our clothes and makes the places where we sleep, under branches, under plastic, sodden.

*

That morning was opaque, Michael remembered later, after it happened, winter crystallising beyond, just out of reach. The mist rubbed off the edges of things but deepened colours. As the drops of water fell, insinuating, the flesh of the tree seemed to him too ripe, too demanding. He found himself waiting beneath acute branches, Jacob behind him, a few hours before the big push.

Sensing an end, they stood under the sparse tree in the unfeeling rain. Though a film of vivid green covered it, in places the bark was divorcing itself from life. Michael could find no words and the boy, trembling, was silent. They were among the dead, Michael disavowing his love.

The longed-for push came. That day the corpses flowered in the red passage and a residue of days of worship flung itself on the hopeless sense.

"Soft, wet under rainfall, like moist hair, the weight and feel of your empty

garments hurts with the smell of you. Spurning your taut love, I shed all grace, though some wear your blood like a medal. With what anguish did you wrestle in that dawn while I remained intact?

No peace is got by abstaining. Words do not breathe. Impotent now to touch or heal your silken wounds, my craving hands are empty."

Michael found him, broken, down in the sap. He lifted the boy, carried him half slung over his back. He could feel Jacob's hip and thigh unnaturally sharp at the base of his spine as they jerked along the muddy passage.

At the trench's end two others came to help him. They found Jacob's wound and were maimed.

Jesus

Crudely they bound his loins with cloths but bone penetrated flesh and shattered testes. Their care was powerless, came too late. His bowels spilled and he died.

Et semini eius

Folds of darkness shrouded the figures and in the marble silence a pitying virgin leant to kiss the dead god, her only son.

Pietà.

*

Yesterday, on the anniversary of my arrival here, I buried my worn manuscript near the wire, keeping out of sight of the soldiers, saying goodbye to Jacob, to Michael. It will rest there, unread but safe until the weapons are gone and we can all go home.

Jack and Alice have come with soup, sandwiches, mince pies and piping hot coffee. We've built up the fire. We talk and hum carols, filling in the words when we can. Women lean together in the play of light: hot faces, cold backs – Ruth kneeling, Jan cross-legged, holding a hot mug in two hands, contemplative. Josie stands a little apart watching the sparks and specks of burnt ash swirl into the night.

I wander over towards the fence and begin to pick up some more wood.

"Hey." I freeze at the sound of a voice just the other side of the wire. His form is obscure. I move away quickly before the familiar obscenities begin but he calls again,

"Wait. Hang on. I – Happy Christmas."

I look into the gloom beyond the wire. A young man's voice.

"Tell the rest of them, too, Happy Christmas."

I can make nothing of his face nor of the sudden acute emotion that this strange meeting at the wire has stirred in me. He says nothing more and is quite still.

"Happy Christmas to you, too," I call into the darkness beyond the perimeter. Pause. Stronger. "To all of you."

I go back to the others with my message. Telling them, I begin to cry. Liz hands me coffee, cake.

As I stare into the flames, my mind returns to that first big action on New Year's Day 1983 when we crossed the perimeter fence. Hurrying to climb the ladders, piling strips of carpet on the barbs, we go over the wire and leap into the base. Josie grabs my hand and we race to beat the rising sun, her feet pounding to my heart. We reach the silo and clamber up. Forty, fifty women, treading the weapons beneath our feet, we link arms, whirling, dancing wildly to the shrieks of our own song. Laughing, we pump the fruit of our peacemaking, tread life into wine, peace into life, defying the world's end.

Extract from

Rainey's Lament

Elizabeth Ridley

Elizabeth Ridley was born in Milwaukee, Wisconsin in 1966. Her first novel, *Throwing Roses,* was published by The Permanent Press; Sag Harbor, New York, in 1993. Her second novel, *The Remarkable Journey of Miss Tranby Quirke,* is published by Virago Press, London, in September 1996.

Thanksgiving Day 1978

Eight-year-old Rainey Astrid McBride slid the yellowed newspaper out of the envelope and carefully read the front page of *The Milwaukee Journal*, dated June 1, 1970. She skimmed over the report about the munitions depot blast that had rattled Saigon, and the advertisement for pantyhose on sale at Gimbels, three pairs for a dollar fifty. Her eyes jumped to the report at the bottom of the page which announced her remarkable entry into the world. She read it aloud to herself, pausing at the end of each sentence. She wanted each word to rise from her lips, float through the roof of the small wooden bungalow and spread throughout the dusty neighbourhood that smelled of tar, burning rubber, and hot ham sandwiches.

HIGH-SCHOOLER GIVES BIRTH
AFTER PLAY-OFF GAME

Mary Jane McBride, 17, of Cudahy, gave birth last night to a healthy 5 lb, 4 oz. baby girl, 15 minutes after helping her basketball team, Emmanuel Lutheran High School, to a 115-89 victory over Our Lady Queen of Peace in the Southeastern Wisconsin Parochial Schools All-Girls Championship League semi-finals.

"I didn't know I was pregnant," McBride said. "I had a cramp at half-time, but I just thought I was dehydrated or something. Because I was tired, Coach only let me play ten minutes of the second half, but I still managed to score 12 points. After the game I was changing in the locker room and I felt like I was going to faint. Then something busted inside me, and I said, 'Oh my Gosh! There's a baby coming! Somebody help me, quick!'"

An ambulance arrived within minutes for a trouble-free delivery. Mother and child are both reportedly doing well this morning at Mount Sinai Hospital.

Officials at Emmanuel Lutheran High School have made it clear that they will not allow McBride to return to classes as a senior this fall. "We do not want to appear to be condoning lascivious and promiscuous behavior by allowing such a student to return to our school. We want to send a clear message - premarital sex among our students will not be accepted," Principal James Howard said.

Having won the semi-finals, Emmanuel Lutheran will meet Gethsemene Lutheran in the finals next Saturday in Oconomowoc.

Rainey bowed her head and tried to recall that moment she couldn't possibly remember. Bouncing around wildly in the hour before her birth and feeling the burn of her mother's struggling muscles, she pictured herself breaking free in a rush of salt water, sliding out onto a cold linoleum floor, opening her eyes and staring up into the faces of sixteen good Lutheran girls in their numbered jerseys, many of whom were unfamiliar with the facts of life, but all of whom must have gazed in wonder at her arrival. It didn't matter who called her a bastard, Rainey told herself, and it didn't matter if Mormor referred to her as a punishment, because this newspaper story was all the proof she needed that she was indeed special, and that she too had a place in God's heart.

Rainey examined the grainy photo of her mother which accompanied the story. She paid particular attention to the dark, sweaty curls framing the bright, angelic face, the broad mouth with its dazzling, dimpled smile, and the freckles that seemed to leap from her skin. Mary Jane looked triumphant, as she must have been. After all, this was the second time she had succeeded in surprising

Mormor. Mary Jane had first surprised Mormor by daring to look so Irish, so much the image of her father, with none of the Scandinavian stamp of Mormor's family – the thin lips, the high-bridged nose, or the long, pale, jutting face.

What had happened between the time of the newspaper article and nine months later, when Mary Jane fled to Escanaba to run a bait-and-tackle shop with a Cuban man named Carlos whom she met at the Greyhound station? What had Mormor done to hurt her daughter so deeply; for clearly; it was Mormor's fault. Mary Jane McBride, this radical bad girl of Cudahy, Wisconsin, was not one to abandon a nine-month-old baby, that much was evident from the photo. Rainey was sure her mother had meant to take her along, meant it with all her heart, but at the last minute she had placed the baby back in the bassinet. It was a supremely sensible thing to do. Mormor and Garth could give the baby a roof over her head, food on the table, stability, good schools, a college education. *All the things we left the Old Country for*, in the oft-repeated family mantra. Mary Jane would have an uncertain future full of tortillas, piñatas, and buckets of icy worms. Rainey saw that her mother had made a great sacrifice in leaving her behind.

"Rainey, are you dressed yet?" Mormor called up the stairs, breaking Rainey's meditation. The door to the attic stairs was open, and in wafted the familiar smell of coffee and curling-irons that sent chills down Rainey's spine. Burnt hair, burnt beans, and rose water lotion – the odours of stoicism which signalled holidays and family events.

"I'm almost ready," Rainey called back.

"Hurry up, we got a long drive ahead of us, and we don't need you slowing us down."

"I'll be ready in a few minutes," Rainey said, more to herself than to Mormor, who had already shut the door. Rainey pressed the photo to her lips and tasted the bitter black ink. "Happy Thanksgiving, Mommy. I'll find you someday," she promised, then slipped the clipping back into the envelope and replaced it in the box under the armoire, where Mormor mistakenly believed it to be well-hidden. Rainey tiptoed down to her bedroom and stood in front of her mirror. Carefully lifting the blue and white pleats of her excessively frilly winter dress, she strapped the vinyl holster around her waist and let her toy gun rest squarely against her hip. She was wearing underpants, bloomers, a petticoat, and a pair of white tights, but even so, the metal felt cold and sharp against her skin. She pressed it into her flesh, right to the bone, and revelled in her toughness. "I'm bringing my little Joe," she said to the face in the mirror. Little Joe, she called it, after her favourite character on *Ponderosa*. "We might just run into Injuns on the way to Owauskeum," she reasoned. "And make no mistake – just because I'm wearing a dress doesn't mean I'm a cry-baby girl." She smoothed down the top layers of her clothing so the gun and holster were hidden under the flouncy fabric of her skirt.

"And just where have you been?" Mormor asked as Rainey bounded down the stairs and into the kitchen. Mormor's long swathe of iron-grey hair had been tightly braided down her back, and the loose hair that had escaped was pinned off her forehead. She wore heavy black liner around her ice-water eyes, and a coral lipstick which cast a dull pallor around her mouth. Her few faded freckles had been dusted with ivory powder, which stuck in the creases of her eyelids and gave her a blurred, uncertain quality which did not fit the intensity of her expression.

"I was working on my book report about the Pilgrims," Rainey answered.

"Liar!" Mormor shouted, and struck Rainey across the mouth with the back of her hand. Rainey felt the cold metal of Mormor's wedding band right between her teeth. "That report is on the table in the den, where you left it last night. Don't you go lying to me, young lady. Now what were you doing?"

"I was watching the Macy's Day Parade on TV," Rainey mumbled, secretly pleased to be exchanging one lie for another. Tears tickled the rims of her eyelids, but she refused to weep. Crying was only for cry-baby girls. Her fingers pressed against the numbness of her mouth, hoping to discover blood, but there was none. Mormor knew how to hit so it would never split a lip, never bruise the skin, even though the pain could reach deep into the bone and settle there, echoing for hours. "I'm sorry. I won't do it again," Rainey said, quivering.

"Make sure that you don't. Now let's go," Mormor said as she and Grandpa Garth piled on their heavy coats and trudged out to the car. Just before the doorway, Rainey stopped. She stared at her speckled face in the mirror, blotchy with shame and swallowed pride, and felt the red pressure of weeping behind her eyes, which she would not release. There was a thrill of pleasure in her chest as she pressed the toy gun secretly into her skin. "I don't like Pilgrims anyway," she told herself.

As they began to slow drive to Owauskeum, Rainey bit her lip bloody but still she did not cry. Milwaukee faded from view, and she pretended she would never see home again. They were heading north toward Sheboygan, hugging the coast of Lake Michigan but far enough inland to be deep into farmland, and she imagined she was discovering the rich countryside for the very first time. Pressing her eye against the frosty window, she could be a Nicolet, Juneau, or Champlain; an explorer charting prairie and moraine. Instead of barns and silos, she saw teepees, circled wagons, and Indian burial mounds.

"Don't breathe on the glass, you'll smudge it up," Mormor said absently as she glanced over her shoulder, but Rainey was far too engrossed in fantasy to hear what she had said. The car was unbearably hot. The heater had been turned up to ten but Mormor and Garth still shivered silently in the front seat. The car smelled of stale tobacco, Ben-Gay, and hot water bottles; odours of old age. Although her Grandparents were only in their mid-fifties, they moved and spoke and spent their days preparing to be much older.

"Do the animals get cold in winter, Mormor?" Rainey asked, looking out at the fields dotted with cows.

"No."

"How come?"

"They've got hair on them," Mormor answered tediously.

"No they don't. Not really," Rainey insisted, suddenly feeling a stab of sympathy for the beasts who stood bravely at their troughs, huddled in wreaths of steamy breath with only their broad backsides as protection against the wind. "If I had a barn, do you know what I'd do? Do you know, Grandpa Garth? I'd build them a fire and put blankets on 'em, and maybe, maybe let them wear sweaters. Look Mormor, do you see that horse over there? Can I get a horse?" Rainey went off on a flight of sympathy and wishes, in love with the rural world she rarely saw in Cudahy.

Suddenly the Oldsmobile wheezed asthmatically, then jerked and pitched forward as Grandpa Garth guided slowly it toward the side of the highway. Other cars honked and angrily sped past them.

"Dang it all anyway," he said, and his stout neck flushed with colour as the car ground to a halt and steam poured from under the bonnet.

"Now look what you've done," Mormor said to Rainey.

"You've gotten his Irish up." They climbed out of the car and onto the hard shoulder. Grandpa Garth popped open the bonnet, took out his red and white checked handkerchief and motioned for Mormor to hand him the water bottle out of the back seat. They both stood peering into the inner workings of the Oldsmobile, sizing up the situation with grim faces and hands on chins, pretending they understood the inner workings of the engine.

Rainey turned away from the highway and faced the broad field with its row of evergreens deep in the background, and a pencil-thin silo off to the side. In front of her was an undulating spread of alfalfa, soy bean, and dead cabbages, their heads dusted with snow like frozen green roses. She stamped her feet for warmth, but her patent leather shoes offered little cover as the cold wind sliced through her tights and nibbled her ankles and the tops of her feet. She drew her arms into her chest and buried her chin deep into her fake fur collar, wincing in pain when the cold zipper brushed her lip. Wait a minute! She had let her guard down! The cold had made her drowsy and inattentive, and now she was vulnerable to attack! Quickly, she tossed up the folds of her skirt, reached under her petticoat, into the holster and drew out Little Joe. She fired at the encroaching Indians who slid silently on their hard brown bellies through the frozen rows of cabbages.

"Bang Bang Bang!" The gunpowder stung her nose and lifted into the chilly air. One, two, three, the Indians arched up briefly in spasms of death, and she watched them fall back into the fields as a lone imaginary arrow wavered in the air and landed in the gravel at her feet.

"If you don't behave, we'll drop you off at the reservation," Mormor threatened, glaring at Rainey from in front of the car.

"Can you?" Rainey asked, intrigued.

"Sure, if you'd rather live with them than with us," Mormor replied.

"I would," she said defiantly, as Grandpa Garth closed the bonnet of the car and motioned for them to climb back inside. He hadn't actually done anything, but he was convinced that the engine had cooled enough that they might make it to Owauskeum.

"Fine. If that's what you want, I'm not complaining," Mormor said as she slammed the door and sliced the seat belt across her body. "Let them feed you, and send you to school, and buy you all those nice things which you never appreciate, and listen to all your damn fool bellyaching."

"I want to go," Rainey said with certainty. "Can you drive me to Oneida? I'd rather go there instead of Black River Falls," she explained, proud of the research she had done about various reservations.

"The Injuns will scalp you, won't they Garth?" Mormor said slowly.

"I 'spose so," he answered dully.

Suddenly the idea seemed to take flight in Mormor's imagination. "They'd like your red hair, hanging from their belt," she began. "Oh yes, I bet that'd fetch a good price, a nice patch of shiny strawberry-blonde."

Rainey blanched, imagining the crown of her skull hollowed out and hanging limply from an Indian's belt. Her head would be a ruby in a row of dusty blond and brown-coloured pebbles, quivering in the light as the Indian's tan arm drew back an arrow. "We could leave next Tuesday," Rainey offered, very quietly. "I don't think we should go before then. I got a math quiz on Monday. And Gretchen Stegner owes me fifty cents because I gave her my eraser." Her scalp prickled and needles tickled her hairline. Nausea swelled in her stomach as a wave of hot, sour air pumped through the car. Rainey imagined a knife slicing through her forehead, and blood dripping onto her blue and white dress. She closed her eyes and fought the burning in her throat, knowing if she vomited on the vinyl seats, Mormor would slap her again.

"Now she's quiet. You've scared the poor girl," Grandpa Garth said, in a voice which revealed nothing, betraying neither sympathy nor satisfaction.

The old Svenson family homestead was located a few miles north of Owauskeum, situated in such a way that it was impossible to pass anything remotely interesting while driving towards it from any direction. All the family resented the house for being so far from where most of them now lived, and this, combined with the general lack of scenery, guaranteed a sour arrival for everyone. The last town they passed before reaching the house was Owauskeum itself, and that was even more desolate than Rainey remembered it. It had once been a thriving paper-mill town, but the mill had closed a generation ago, taking with it all signs of life and liveliness, reducing it to a desert of sheet metal and concrete. All that remained of the mill was the looming brick smokestack and the strange scent like a honey-roasted ham which hung in the air on humid days as a bittersweet reminder of the town's past prosperity. What was left of the grass was perpetually overgrown, and even the bent mailboxes and twisted laundry lines had faded from the years of dust, salt, and sun. As they drove through town, Rainey felt the ghosts of Thanksgivings past, when packs of immigrant families must have gathered here to celebrate, and the streets and porches and doorways would have been warm and bright with handshakes, pine fires, and thick winter coats.

Turning off of the main road, Grandpa Garth manoeuvred onto a gravel track marked with a small sign that read, 'CCC' and led into a field. Stalks of dying corn shriveled and swooned on either side of the car, and Rainey felt closed in by the dry rustle of leaves, reaching out to touch her like so many pleading fingers. She leaned her shoulder against the seatback and looked out the back window and up into the clean, drained sky which was scrubbed of cloud cover. It was certain to snow. She was proud of knowing that, of her ability to feel the shift in the wind. Autumn moved to winter very quickly here, once the smell of burning leaves filled the air, and hard things pumpkins, squash, and knotted gourds, sprouted from the frozen ground. Something crackled in the distance as cold things broke, and Rainey thought she could hear the sap hardening in the veins of the trees, and taste the phantom flavour of Christmas maple sugar candy.

The dead field split open as the car broke free of the corn. They drove up to the house which was an old-style Victorian homestead, ornate and artificial, with whitewash windows and spiked gingerbread trim. Half a dozen cars were parked haphazardly around the perimeter in a broken circle of broad-backed Fords and Buicks, ranging in colours from tan to brown to mustard yellow.

"I see Hen bought himself a Cadillac," Mormor said. "Where he got the money from, I just don't know."

"Maybe he won it playing Bingo," Grandpa Garth said, in his usually inscrutable voice. Rainey couldn't wait to get out of the car. She thrilled at the thought of the upper room at the top of the old staircase, a place of mystery and possible sin. Every year she and her cousins would climb the creaky wooden stairs and play in that room for hours, hypnotized by the heady incense of attics, old aunts, and hat boxes.

"Rainey, you better behave this year or else," Mormor warned before they got out of the car.

"Or else what?" she asked defiantly, although she knew full well what Mormor meant. On Thanksgiving of the previous year, Rainey had argued with her cousins, the twins Katrina and Karina. "My Mommy says your Mommy is a fly buzzing in hell and all the other flies are eating her right now," Katrina had taunted Rainey while they played in the upper room.

"They are not," Rainey insisted.

"Are so," said Karina.

"Are not."

"Are so."

"Oh yeah?" Rainey said, rising to the challenge. "Well if my Mommy is in hell then your dolls are going to be in the sewers." She grabbed Katrina and Karina's matching Baby-Burps-And-Wets-Alot dolls and ran down to the bathroom, where she held the dolls' plastic heads under the water while she flushed the toilet again and again. When the twins told Mormor what Rainey was doing, Mormor ran upstairs and grabbed Rainey, slapping her hard behind the knees, and then marched her downstairs, soggy dolls in hand, to apologize to everyone for ruining the twins' Thanksgiving. The worst part was not the apologizing, but the inevitable whispers that followed her the rest of the evening.

"What do you expect? She's her mother's child through and through."

"Pity the poor girl. She deserves pity, not scorn."

But Rainey had held her head high even as she felt Mormor's handprint darken and swell on the skin behind her knees. She would not give anyone the satisfaction of seeing her cry, even though her eyes pinched and her throat ached as if she had swallowed an apple whole and it had lodged half-way down to her heart. Instead she got her revenge after supper by kicking Katrina and Karina under the table, and when they began to wail, she gobbled up their slivers of sweet pecan pie.

"You'll behave young lady, or else you'll be sitting out in the car eating Thanksgiving dinner all by yourself," Mormor warned, and Rainey, although unwilling to make any promises, nodded her head yes.

"Sonja, Garth, Rainey, welcome. Happy Thanksgiving," Aunt Ingebjorg said jovially as she answered the door and ushered them inside. Once they had stepped into the foyer they were immediately swallowed up in the hub of noisy activity. Plates, pots, and dishes danced from hand to hand, chairs squeaked and slid across the waxed wooden floor, and red-cheeked children unrolled balls of tinsel while a striped kitten darted from lap to lap. The house was densely humid and all the windows had been opened, in spite of the cold. The crippled tree which pressed against the side of the house was creeping surreptitiously into the sitting room on its fingertips of gnarled twigs. A few first snowflakes had softened the windowsill and drifted to the floor, sticking to the curtains and shining like beads of light.

The women of the house were anonymous in a flurry of arms and pots and aprons, with fine layers of perspiration on their lips and chins and hairlines, while the men were idle as usual, watching the football game on TV and arguing gloomily about fishing, guns, and race relations over their cans of Schlitz and Old Milwaukee. Uncle Arne played with the electric knife, pretending to cut off his arm, to the delighted screams of Rainey's dozens of cousins.

"Sonja, Garth, glad you could make it," Ingebjorg said. "And Rainey, how's my little tiger?"

Rainey blushed happily. She loved Aunt Ingebjorg more than anyone else, and secretly wished Ingebjorg would adopt her. Never married, tall, and squarely-built, Ingebjorg had short, pale hair pressed close to her head, and rosy cheeks that made her look like a kind of Mrs Claus. Rainey wanted to fall into the folds of her arms and be pressed against that solid neck, maybe even submit to a kiss on the cheek. She wanted to go back to Chippewa Falls, where Ingebjorg taught third grade and led the local 4-H Club.

"I'm okay," Rainey said, still blushing. "Guess what? I got an 'A-plus-plus' on my report about, 'Millard Fillmore – Our Unappreciated President.'"

"Excellent! *De var fint!* I'm glad to see you have repented for your evil ways," Ingebjorg kidded. "Perhaps Katrina and Karina will show you their new dolls."

"I'm trying extra hard to be a good girl," Rainey replied in a tone of voice which understood Ingebjorg's humour, and still managed to mock Mormor's warning about her behaviour.

"Rainey's been told. If she isn't a good girl, Santa won't come this Christmas," Mormor said evenly.

"I want a BB gun," Rainey suddenly burst out.

"For shame Rainey! You'll get no such thing. BB guns are not for little girls. You'll shoot your eye out," Mormor warned. Ingebjorg laughed.

"Can I go upstairs now?" Rainey asked, suddenly tired of adult conversation and longing to re-discover the wonders of the attic.

"What do you say?" Mormor insisted.

"Can I please go upstairs?"

"Go on," Ingebjorg said, patting Rainey's shoulder as she skipped towards the staircase.

"That child is a nightmare sometimes," Rainey heard Mormor say to Ingebjorg. "The Good Lord is punishing me, and she's my cross to bear."

*

When Rainey clattered down the staircase two hours later, so engrossed in an old fur coat she had found that she hadn't heard Aunt Thelma's first three attempts to call her to supper, she was immediately enveloped in the strange and serious silence of the dining room. Her steps slowed and quieted as she neared the landing, realizing that she was somehow entering a room very different from the one she had left earlier. The football game was still on the television, but the volume had been turned down to a whisper, rising only slightly when someone scored a touchdown, and the frantic plates and pots and spoons had stopped their singing, and now waited on the table with an air of gracious expectation.

All the aunts and uncles and cousins stood stiffly behind their seats, even blind Farfar Jens, who stared into the pale candle flame and clutched his hand-carved chairback which trembled slightly and tapped against the floor. Rainey walked self-consciously down the aisle of stern-eyed relatives who seemed to be rebuking her for keeping them waiting. She slid into her spot at the children's end of the table, next to Aunt Ingebjorg. "How was the upper room?" Ingebjorg whispered, squeezing Rainey's hand and giving her a secret smile, as if she already knew the answer, and had been with her discovering the fractured ornaments, the coonskin cap, the yellowed wedding-dress, and the box of tarnished coins and beads.

"Oh, I found a–" she started, but she was cut off by Uncle Torgrim, who tapped his glass, calling everyone to attention.

"We would like to now give thanks for this bountiful meal which the good Lord has had the grace to set down before us, rude sinners that we are. We would like to thank Him for the blessings of this past year, and pray that He may grant us peace, happiness, and prosperity in the months to come. *I Jesu navn, går vi til bord, spise og drikke, på dit ord. . . "* Rainey listened to the rhythm of the Norwegian table prayer, trying to pin down the strange feeling that floated above her. She watched the people beside her, noticing their creased eyelids, their down-turned mouths, their solid hands. They were farmers, farmer's wives, and sons and daughters of farmers who, even though they worked in offices in cities and towns, still had the soil worked deep into their skin. She watched the candlelight reflect off the polished silver which had been carried years ago in a wooden crate from Norway, and she studied the delicate needlework of the Hardanger napkins, folded like wings above each plate. She felt a current of connection run through herself and these people. She was one of them, and yet completely separate. The thought surprised her. She felt off-balance, as if lifted briefly and set down again in a deft gesture which no one else noticed, and she was nearly, but not exactly, in the spot where she had been before. The disturbance of the dust around her feet seemed to prove this, and she shivered with a secret sense of herself.

" . . .forever and ever Amen," Uncle Torgrim ended in English, and everyone ended with him, so that the shared 'Amen' echoed like a bell and rose above the table, drifting higher and higher until it melted into air. "Amen," Rainey whispered, and as she said it, the word became real. A chalice inside her spilled as she did give thanks. For what, she was not certain. *A God who thinks of me. Yes. Why not? Even me.*

She looked at the table with suddenly unfamiliar eyes, and was overwhelmed with the density of the meal. There was so *much* of everything, she thought, as she gazed at the vat of mashed potatoes glistening with puddles of butter, the steaming tureens of cream corn, the kettle of butternut squash soup balanced over the glowing Bunsen burner. She watched the slightly sweaty quiver of the jello moulds with their flecks of pineapple, carrot, marshmallow, and lime. Rainey closed her eyes and filled her head with the scent of the cooked birds, the cranberries, and the stuffing of raisin, walnut, and rum, and the pies; pumpkin, pecan, cherry, and apple, stacked on cooling racks with steam still escaping from their centres, and on either side of the pie plates, cups of frozen custard and small dishes of cinnamon-speckled *rommegrot.*

The food seemed unbelievably rich, too rich, too luxurious, too lavishly drenched with giblet gravy to belong to this table; unfit to serve such stern and unforgiving people. Only the *lefse* and *lutefisk* seemed to belong to them. That was their true food, those concoctions of codfish, potatoes, and lye. But Rainey chose not to think of that, preferring to meditate on thankfulness, and the way it had suddenly become real.

And then, just as Uncle Arne was about to slice into the succulent turkey, giving it practised taps with the electric knife, there was a rush of noise outside – sleigh-bells and doors slamming and the dull mad stamping of snow-covered feet. The sun had struck the lake in such a way that to look towards the back window was to be temporarily blinded, but as Rainey looked and looked and looked, the dim figure of a boy, about her own size and age, gradually emerged. He glided through the door silently, effortless in his snow-softened boots, and stopped in the centre of the room. He was covered with a glittering layer of snow which dusted his cap and scarf and buttons like fine powdered sugar, and as Rainey watched him blink and shiver, she felt a dazzling sweetness sting her lips and tongue.

The boy pulled off his cap and brushed the snow from his magnificent coat. This coat was like no coat she had ever seen in Milwaukee. This coat was double-breasted and made of dark blue felt with a broad folded collar and red and white ribbon worked into the trim. The cuffs and epaulettes were also trimmed with shiny ribbon. The coat boasted four oversized pockets, and the pocket over the left breast had some kind of crest on it. The design on the crest appeared to be an intertwined figure of an anchor, a flag, a snake, and a crown. This was no ordinary coat, and clearly, this was no ordinary boy. He would have to be a prince, a knight, some sort of junior duke. He was destined to inherit the kingdom and rule the whole world. Rainey decided, finally, that she was gazing on nothing less than the future king of Wisconsin. She bowed her head, but kept her eyes focused on the round softness of his face.

The boy was accompanied by an adult on either side, although it had taken her several long moments to notice them. These two, a man and a woman, were vague, tall, square people with fading grey and blond complexions, but they made virtually no impression beyond that. Parents probably, Rainey surmised, but how could such plain people give birth to this vision? Rainey was aware of the others at the table, and how their attention was directed to the strikingly blond little boy whose eyes were pale as oysters, almost white in their centres, but rimmed with iridescent blue ink. His skin had been burnished by the wind, and a blush of scarlet beat in his cheeks.

"Who is that?" Rainey asked Aunt Ingebjorg beside her. She trembled as she reached for Ingebjorg's hand.

"Why, that's your cousin Andy," Ingebjorg whispered back. She too seemed taken aback by his sudden appearance, and the way everyone seemed compelled to stare at him.

"There's a bunch of chairs out on the porch," someone said. "Pull up a few and make yourself at home."

"Andy, there's room for you at the kids' end of the table," Mormor said, pointing to the empty seat beside Rainey.

None of the three figures stepped forward, and the room remained strangely still. The boy moved only enough to whisk off his long red scarf with a theatrical flourish, and before the many winding folds of silk had unfurled and settled against his chest, he had his hands placed firmly on his hips, and an imperial and insolent look gleamed brightly in his eyes. "My name," he said, in a high-pitched and richly-accented voice, "is no longer Andy. My name is Ambrose Torsten Dienst."

A Handful of Marbles

Paul Saxton

Paul Saxton was born in Nottingham in 1967. He lives with Mairi and their two children, Tom and Louie.

My mother sat lonely in her chair and said: What is it that brings me such bad luck? Am I to suffer at his hands for always?

I gazed from her bedroom window to the doorstep below. Her husband, my father, lay frozen and oh so chilly blue. He had been dead for three weeks. We buried him in the cemetery on the other side of town. He returned as a zombie. His intention may have been to reach the key through the letterbox. He was caught fast.

Never mind mother, I said, we'll have you out of here before you draw your next breath.

My brother entered to see if she needed mopping. A lime green bucket filled with warm water hung from his arm. He is generally the nervous type but that night he excelled in confidence.

My mother said: Your father – you are the spitting embodiment.

My brother frowned himself to attention. He was unsure whether to take her observation as a compliment. He was young. We tried to keep hidden from him the fact that our father had dabbled with Hoodoo spices. He applied a dripping sponge to my mother's forehead.

My mother said: But your sister – she has a little of me.

I smiled. There is a resemblance between us.

My mother rose and cast a cautious eye to the bedraggled figure below.

She said: He was once a good-looking man. He was enough to turn my head.

That was true. I have seen the photographs. I can understand how she loved him blindly for a time. Some men belong to black and white.

173

I looked down at my father and wondered over his predicament.

My grandfather maintained that his daughter drove a silver dagger through his heart when she accepted my father.

A monster! he wailed, a man not fit for the company of swine!

But still, in the early stages there was more than love between them.

My mother said: Wherever we stepped we invigorated everything in our path. While walking in streets and alley-ways we softened steel and rounded the edges of concrete.

She said: We visited pet shops to warm the blood of the reptiles.

The first few months of their marriage were trouble-free. My father worked all day and my mother waved him off every morning. Everything swam. A happier household was unlikely to be found. And then she announced over breakfast that she was carrying his child. My father skulked at the news. My mother sighed herself into a future that promised little.

By the time I was born my father was a stranger to her. She would never know where he was, what he had done and how many calories he had taken in. So her attention fell to me.

She complained that it wouldn't have killed him to have taken an interest. That instead of lounging wherever he lounged he could have been at home with me warming his lap. He should have been telling me stories and combing my hair. He should have whispered how much he loved me and how I was his golden little girl. But he never did.

She said: Obsessed with himself. Forever washing his hands in fear of a contamination. Those people he moved with. I should have heeded the signs. I should have left him when you and I were young.

What prevented you? I said.

She twisted uneasily: Ah, what a question. Who knows? He was a man. I expected little.

My father groaned. My mother stood quickly. An approximation of horror beat about her face.

She cried: He stirs! He refuses to rest! What is it that he wants?

He was regaining strength. The sun was coming up. His colour had changed. His blueness melted towards orange. Even with his eyes glazed I could tell he was getting excited about something. I imagined the worst.

My mother, more hopeful, said: Perhaps he means us no harm. Perhaps he has returned to atone. Perhaps he seeks to make it up to me in some way.

She is foolish like that sometimes. She tries to see the good in everyone. Even after all she's been through.

But mother, I said, look at his face. Look at the way anger and hatred have riddled it with wounds. See how he spits bile. Regard him closely.

She stared at him. She considered her husband.

She said: Such a clever girl. You are right. If only I had your brains. We should move away to somewhere he can't find us.

And within five minutes we three were stepping over him, braving the curses that flew from his blood-stained lips.

In the new room my mother brushed the curtains aside. The light pleased her. She told my brother and I to sit. She said we should pay attention. She said that in a moment, when her head was empty of rubbish, she would tell us how our father had turned.

She paced for a while. Once she had worn herself out she sat. For only then was it worth her while to do so.

She said: Your father wanted to belong. He liked a crowd. I first saw him leaping like an idiot from one horse to another. We were both on the merry-go-round, although not together.

She stood and twirled. Her pirouette reminded us of a merry-go-round. She fell dizzy into her chair.

She said: Later I saw him again. My mother and father saw him too. They took an instant dislike. They weren't happy to witness the suggestive gestures he made with a candy-floss. I was strangely impressed. I was a younger girl than I am now. I said to him: If you are thinking of courting, then you would be wise to knock at my door. And knock he did.

She rapped on the arm of her chair to show us how he knocked. It was an unusual knock. The kind of knock that is somehow full of significance. When I knock it sounds as though I just need to be let in.

She said: He was full of life then – so handsome. He had the Cary Grant about him. All the girls had a thing for him. They would have been happy to be his. On our first date he gave me a handful of marbles. They looked like eyeballs. Idiot that I am, I thought they were made simply of glass. For foresight, for a premonition I should have begged. But I was young, I knew no better. He was already moving within the Hoodoo.

My brother was perplexed. He had no idea what my mother was referring to. He looked to me for help.

Shh, I said, let her finish. I'm sure she will reveal all when the time is right.

Reveal what? he said. As far as I'm concerned there's nothing to say. Dad's gone. It doesn't matter anymore. I'm going out. I'll be drunk by the time I get back.

That was likely. My brother, if nothing else, was easy and familiar with alcohol. I began to protest.

My mother waved that I should let him go.

She said: A boy. He knows where he lies. He will return.

We were in a safe-house. A three-storey terrace in the middle of an unfamiliar city. The Sisters of the Victims of Supernatural Vice provided us with shelter. They understood our situation. They told us not to worry.

We are warm and together here, said the dwarf director. We are women who have suffered at the hands of goblins, fairies, golems and zombies. Lights out at ten and no talking after ten-thirty.

My mother was unhappy. She was fifty-two years old and tired of being treated like a child. She gazed longingly at the world on the other side of the window. Her breath made condensation on the glass. When it was impossible to see any longer she climbed into bed. Her sighs were deep.

She said: My father warned me. To have listened – that would have been a good thing. Obstreperous girl that I was. You should always pay attention to your father. I laughed at this. The irony was lost on her. She seemed to have forgotten that her husband was my father. I liked that.

We sat together all day. Not more than two sentences passed between us. By evening we were hungry. The two women left in charge suggested we eat out.

We can't, I said, my father is looking for us. He could be shuffling down the street at this very moment.

The two women, who were twins though not sisters, said this was unlikely. They claimed their agents were watching my father closely. Although he was too powerful to stop, they could at least veer him off course.

My mother said: We will get food and search for your brother.

My brother is four years younger than I. Which made him eighteen at the time. He was, at heart, a nice boy. But he had the same underdeveloped mind that most eighteen-year-old boys have. Still, he could have been worse. My father loved him less than he loved me. Which was hardly at all.

My mother told me that my brother was conceived without my father's knowledge, just after his first attack. She visited him in hospital. He was comatose and not likely to stir for another month. She took him as he lay silent and peaceful. She said it was the last time they had fun together.

She worried about my brother. She imagined that he too would fall foul of the Hoodoo curses.

We looked for him in the pubs and clubs. He was nowhere to be found. My mother passed on a photograph of him as a baby. Nobody recognized him. By midnight we were ready to give up the search and return to the house. But then we remembered the curfew and the dwarf's warnings. My mother damned little people everywhere.

My brother failed to return. We discovered that he'd joined the Navy.

My mother said: That boy. Too much like your father. I should have taken him in hand.

I thought she was a little harsh. It seemed to me that he hadn't any choice. What else could he do but sail the seven seas with a kitbag full of magazines? He was in good company. The other men would look after him. They stick together like that.

We informed the dwarf that we were unhappy with her service. She squeaked in surprise and said ingratitude was not a virtue. She made a fuss out of the fact that we hadn't offered her payment. Like we had money to throw around. We had enough to enable our escape. The dwarf asked us to leave.

Just after he died my mother sat down and worked out what my father had left us. She thought we'd at least be comfortable. She was disappointed. The authorities wanted her to find employment.

My mother said: I'd sooner have cancer.

So they refused to give her a penny.

She said: Imagine! After years of sweat and toil bringing up two children and dancing with a madman I am expected to fend for myself. What am I, a dog without a master?

She was right. My father had always prevented her from taking a job. He said it was a man's thing. She argued that she could do as she pleased. He said he'd like to see her try. And then he punched her so that she fell to the ground.

It was lucky for him that she hated him enough already.

For a while we considered leaving the country. We thought he would think twice about following us. We thought a corpse would be noticed on a plane or a boat. No doubt he'd be stopped at customs. But then mother remembered that my father was the resourceful type. That even in a state of ataxy a raft wouldn't be too much trouble for him.

Despite having a husband and father as one, we had little idea of what constituted a zombie. The questions that ran through our minds: How do you kill a zombie? What are they vulnerable to? Do they remember being alive, and if so, is it this that accounts for their bad tempers? Do they eat? Do they eat people? Have they any loyalty to their family? Do they decay as they go on? Do they like music? Do they drink to excess? What is their relationship with ghosts? Presented with a choice of directions – right or left – which one would they take? Do they have an interest in the opposite sex? Do they feed like vampires in order to survive? Are they affected by illness? Do they cry? Do they laugh? Where do they go when we don't see them? What do their mothers think of them? Do they walk in beauty like the night? How can you distinguish between a zombie and a normal dead person? Are they good with children? Would you want one living next door?

It was difficult to accept that my father was a part of the zombie culture. My mother explained that he had planned it. He had spent years in preparation.

She said: He had another woman – a Hag. She had the Hoodoo touch. She greased him with a terrapin. I was told to avoid him until he went back to her. When he went back they fornicated, the grease still on him. Nine months later that woman died. They cut her open. From her liver hung three terrapins.

She said: After that your father carried sacks. To collect black cats. He boiled them alive. The bones he took to the river. He waited. And then one day the devil rose foamy. He shook your father's hand.

She said: He had frogs in his pockets. He loitered at crossroads. He became big with The Clan. He would run around the house seven times and then turn to look over his left shoulder. He would talk again with the devil. He scrawled his name. He was taken. He was taken a long time before he died. He was a husband and a father. He was a man.

A few years before he turned my mother's face into a map of pain and worry, my father announced that he wanted his marbles back. My mother was a little surprised.

She said: Your love is over so soon?

No, he replied, I need to roll them between finger and thumb. Here, see.

On every digit were markings of the like she'd never seen before.

Ah, he said, a new tattoo parlour in town. They specialize in good fortune. Those patterns are emblematic of something. I forget what.

He explained that his fingers were tender and that the cool polished glass of a marble would be just the thing to soothe them. My mother handed them over. She told him to be careful. And off he went to the bedroom, closing the door behind.

After six hours she began to wonder. A knock provoked no response. So she entered. My father sat cross-legged on the bed, totally naked except for a colourful length of beads that hung around his neck. He seemed to be dead to the world. On closer inspection my mother realized that the necklace was made up of the marbles he'd asked for earlier. Each one of them seemed to stare accusingly at her. She left him to it.

Within a week she'd noticed a change. He seemed to be lighter in spirit. More handsome too. She followed him one day when he was supposed to be at work. She crept through the door of a house to see him circled by a group of six or seven naked men. They were anointing him with powder and sticky liquid. She left them to it.

When he came home later that evening she confronted him.

She said: So, the bane of my sweet short life has returned at last.

He laughed.

Yes, he said, I am back to the bosom of my wife who bleats like a toadfrog. I should hang you over the fireplace to dry you out.

She replied: Rich stuff coming from a husband with the knees of a bandy.

My father sat down and demanded food.

She said: There is none. All I have is this bowl of stew. Prepared with you in mind.

He looked into the steaming dish. He aged six and a half years. His face turned at the corners. He stood quickly and shook his fist.

See this? he bellowed, It is yours! A gift from me! No charge!

My mother ducked sharply as he punched his way towards her. His knuckles made heavy contact with the wall. A layer of skin fell from his hand.

He passed out. Clean away all over the kitchen floor. The next day my brother was conceived.

Over the years my father grew worse. He denied the possibility of polite conversation. My brother and I succumbed to his indifference.

My mother said: I struggled to keep heartache from the view of my children.

She took the weight of chastisement as if she had been raised with broad shoulders. My father delivered physical punishment as if it were a habit.

He was visited by frequent pain. His first attack left him with a pallor. The second gave him dust under the eyes. The third removed his dignity.

But they were a blessing.

My mother said: They got him out of the house. There is nothing worse than a man – however good – forever under your feet.

During those months when the doctors sought to heal him, we stayed home to loaf. On those days my mother laughed a laugh that vibrated church bells everywhere. She knew what it was to harness beauty. Her thoughts nestled with the birds.

She said: Under every stretch of tarmac there is a meadow of daisies.

We were happy to believe her.

Our flight from zombie retribution was not without its pleasures. My mother and I wondered if the odd glance back might be enough to keep us from harm. For a time we daydreamed. We hoped we were safe. But my father's cadaverous sighs reached us when we least expected them.

We moved in circles. Somebody told us that the zombie notion of return was tempered by their desire to embrace straight lines. Deviations are not their concern.

My mother said: Your father lumbered when he was alive. Why should he change now?

I wondered whether the dwarf's agents were still upon him. Although she was small she had determination. I imagined she could well be our salvation. My mother disagreed.

She said: Her size prevents her growth. She will have forgotten us by now. Her heart is in miniature.

When the travelling and the lack of money became too much we returned home. The house was as I remembered it. My father had left his hand in the letterbox. My mother placed it on the mantelpiece.

She said: A memento – in case we never see him again.

For me that could have only been a good thing. But my mother was tired.

She said: Why run? He will find us anyway. We should welcome him. A wife and a daughter have certain responsibilities.

And then she sat down as if she intended never to get up again.

You should take stock, I said, you should look around and see what you have.

My mother sucked in air. She closed her eyes.

She said: For the chance to be young again. I would give a right arm.

But you still have a life ahead of you, I reasoned.

She grew pale and said: It is always the course that women take. A ride over the trenches that men have dug for us. We should take away their spades. But if it were only that simple. A smile is not enough to get us through the days.

My mother slept as I explored the house. I knew the last room I'd take would be the cellar. A place where my father often retired.

Today you are sixteen, my father once said. Yesterday was your last day as a child. Today is the start of something else. I cannot advise, only warn. But you love me. Whatever I say will present you with difficulties.

He was right. He left me with curiosity. I realized that I was forever curled up inside him. Even though I longed for escape.

My mother once told me: When all has finished, he is, after all, your father. You elected him to that role. I was a party to it.

I never forgave her for that.

My mother said: Your father, he grasped for death. He thought it the same as the stars. Up there, the stratosphere beckoning, he saw his firmament. We were a block to flights of fancy. He resented us. We were earth bound. The sun wore his face.

Before his final attack, the one that sent him to death, my father came home with a suitcase.

My mother said: Why the gunny bag?

My father smiled, he was in the final throes.

It is for my property, he said, I know there's not much but whatever is mine I'll take. Orders of the doctor. The wishes of The Clan. I don't question.

My mother replied: Slam the door behind you. So I know you've gone.

Oh, you'll know when I've gone, he said, you'll notice I left on the day I return.

My mother said: Return? Where's the good in that?

My father raised his voice. It was a tactic of course. My mother was unimpressed.

Look! he cried, You know I've been mysterious lately. I know you haven't time for me. I'm the enigmatic sort. I move around you. You're stationary as I circle you. I've decided to go. Important stuff calls me.

My mother said: So go. You expect me to beg? Go. I've had cigarettes as better company than you.

My father put his hands around her thigh.

You know, he murmured, I think I've always loved you.

My mother stroked his hair with a bread knife.

She said: Love? Pah! This is you: Hatred? Yes please! Anger? Thank you! Cynicism? I'll take it!

She said: Get your hands off my person.

My father slid to the other side of the kitchen. He tried to look hurt.

Okay, don't push it, he said, I'm going.

He filled the suitcase. It was too heavy for him. His limbs were weak.

My mother said: You need a hand with the sack? Tell it to the pals you lurk with.

He dragged the suitcase into the garden and returned to my mother.

One final kiss? he said.

He slurred this part. His eyes rolled about his head. His teeth gathered momentum. The sweats lubricated him. He fell to his knees.

Away! he raged, It is happening at last. The moment I've been waiting for all these years. That made me treat you so. I'm not sad. I'd do it all again. They know, they know where a man's heart lies. They know indeed. Goodbye!

And with that he punched my mother until she crumpled into unconsciousness. He left dust trails behind. She swept them up the following morning.

At his funeral The Clan gathered around the coffin. The lid had been left open. My father lay with his eyes wide and staring. Moths' wings sat on his forehead. The Clan mumbled. They were working at the Hoodoo. They circled his box. Each in turn bent to kiss him through their twisted mouths. Then they screwed him in.

My mother and I were confused and amused. To us The Clan were peddlers. They were men. Ordinary men. Not a handsome one between them. Dust hung from their eyes.

An announcement tannoyed around the room: To a husband and father who has since departed. A man without a life. But a man even in death.

When they came to lift my father's coffin they found it too heavy to carry. It took twelve men to move it from the church into the cemetery outside. It grew heavier. Blood seeped from the sides. The coffin was rested and the lid prised open. A black cat sat on my father's chest. It was combing his hair with its paw.

My mother said: On the day of his death I skipped down the street like a little girl in pigtails. Without him, it was like seeing the sun for the first time. I never imagined that freedom could be just one corpse away.

I nearly broke my neck when I ventured into the cellar. My father had laid a trap. A single marble sat on each step, ready to roll its victim asunder. At the bottom lay a bath of acid. And then I realized. Was this the best he could do? This man, whom I had feared since I could hear? Was he simply too wrapped up in himself? He had always underestimated us. To him we were figments.

I ran to my mother. She lay in the middle of the floor. Her eyelids were closed tight. I fingered them open.

She said: In sleep I am as empty. Nothing protects me.

Nonsense, I said, I have his downfall mapped out. We will welcome him when he returns.

We sat together for three weeks. We knew he would come. We huddled for warmth. All of the furniture, all of the trappings of the past, lay in ruins in the garden. We needed nothing except each other.

The fourth week brought us news. A dwarf sauntered up the path and asked to be let in. We recognized him but couldn't be sure.

I believe you were once friendly with my sister, he said as he sat on the mantelpiece.

He scratched his chin with my father's hand.

My sister is a good woman, he said, she told me of your woes. My heart went out. I'm here to help.

My mother said: A big problem tackled by a midget?

The dwarf flushed red. He reached into his pocket and pulled out a small green bottle.

This is a cure, he said, I could drink it at any time. Within a few seconds I would be your superior in height. But I will never take it. I'm comfortable with myself.

But why carry it around? I said.

Because, he replied, there are people out there who are smaller than I. Pity them.

He was right. The world is full of tiny folk.

The dwarf taught us the ways of the zombie. We were eager pupils. We had to be ready for my father's attack.

My mother said: From beyond the grave even. Why me?

The dwarf read to us every night. He was a zombie scholar. He hated them. His father, brother and uncle were all dead for a while.

When a zombie turns, he said, what is left of his eyes fails to take in the world. When he thinks of himself he doesn't imagine any other positions. He paints himself into corners and forgets to take balls of twine into labyrinths. He is always parallel to himself. The zombie is often morose and petulant, although he is wary of having emotions attributed to him. In death he is much the same as he was in life. He is temperamental and yappy. He needs to be coaxed and soothed.

My father burst through the kitchen door on a Friday evening, exactly a month after the dwarf's arrival. He had changed considerably. Where once were set dead, yellow eyes there was now nothing but the infinite emptiness of black sockets. His mouth too, which stretched to the stumps of his ears, contained nothing but dripping copper-coloured gums. He smiled.

You think this is bad! he shouted, You should see my genitals!

He roared with laughter.

My mother said: What do you want? My days are short for trivialities.

He gazed through her as if she were not even in the room. He turned his attention to me.

Daughter! he cried, Have you gone too!?

I held out the marbles I'd taken from the cellar steps. His sockets dilated. He eased one foot towards me.

They are mine, he growled, give them to me.

He rocked forward. I stepped back. I held the marbles tightly. He lunged. An arm fell to the floor. He was ebbing.

The dwarf took the marbles and placed them in a stone circle. They shrank and vanished, leaving only traces of silver.

My father glowed.

Be careful, cried the dwarf, he is Jack Mulatta! Beware of his light. He wants to tantalize you.

My father grew horns. The dwarf threw soil into his face.

The earth from your grave – from an evildoer's grave, the dwarf said. You will burn!

My father shed his skin to escape the pain.

Quick! the dwarf cried, the salt, the pepper! Sprinkle them on his skin! Do it now!

My mother did as he said. We stood back as my father, confused and frightened, stumbled around the kitchen. He tried to climb back into his skin. The smell of burning flesh filled the room. He sank to the floor and begged for release.

But I am back, he implored, a second time is all I crave. I was mistaken. I love you all!

He tore at his flesh, pulling chunks away. Terrapins hung from his organs. He screamed in pain.

We left him there and stepped out into the night. From the house we could hear his cries. They didn't matter anymore. We had stopped listening. We sprinkled evil graveyard dirt over the doors and window frames. My mother dug a small hole and placed cayenne pepper, sulphur and a clove of garlic within.

She said: It was the last meal. He refused to eat it. He will feed on it for eternity now.

From the east, Hags of all shape and size descended upon the house and rode my father until he was nothing but dust.

The dwarf kissed us both goodbye. We said we'd miss him. He told us not to worry. He said that on the feet of angels sat the little people. We smiled at the thought.

My mother said: We will look out for you. Remember us when you're tall.

The dwarf vanished.

My mother said: You see what kind of a man your father was? Six feet tall and yet you would mistake him for somebody shorter.

She said: Your life. Use it wisely. Who am I but a foolish woman? Who am I to advise? Steer clear of them.

Of who? I said.

She picked up a small stone and threw it towards the embers of the house.

She said: Who knows? They are all the same to me.

My mother and I continued to tread the road we'd swept so many times before. The trick was to never look back. Sometimes, when we did, we could see my brother, tiny against the horizon. We gestured fondly. Next to him stood my father and The Clan. They seemed uncomfortable, a little sorry even. We could have cared less. We were truly free of them.

As time passed they were brushed into the corners where we knew we wouldn't step.

The thing about zombies is they like you to know they are there.

So you can turn and say: I have a zombie on my trail.

The other thing about zombies is they are only re-animated corpses. There is little that is magic about them. Without the pump of a heart their blood settles in their shoes. They are slovenly and mealy-mouthed as a result.

And although zombies are often fearful and fiery in appearance, they can be frozen by a glance from their children.

They are dust.

Extract from

The Hammer, Sickle & Sun

Lisa Selvidge

Lisa Selvidge is a graduate of Russian Language & Literature. Born in Leicester in 1966, she has also lived in Berlin, Tokyo and Moscow. She is currently working on a film adaptation of Bulgakov's *Master & Margarita* with Carrie Worrall and a novel, *Gods at War.*

1. Trans-Siberia

As the train lurched further eastwards, Volodia was sitting inside a box of cabbages clutching his belly. He had been travelling for thousands of kilometres and, in addition to the dirt and stench of alcohol, putrescent vegetables, Russian tobacco and his own crepitations, he now had diarrhoea. This fetid cocktail of pungent fluids and odours emitted such a foul stink that the whole of Siberia howled in protest. But the howling winds only made Volodia excrete more rancid pellets of fear into the dark box as the train charged along the iron road, taking him further and further away from his home. He sat there, body poised, braced for anything that might try and catch him unawares. Volodia had to be very cautious because everyone was trying to kill him. Even the half-frozen mangy cabbages had attacked him when the train, waggling its body from side to side, had sent them flying on top of him. In revenge, he had eaten as many as he could without vomiting, but he was still trapped inside the box. Now, in his cavernous hole, all he could do was sit and wait and listen to the sound of the train.

Chuckety-chuck. Chuckety-chuck. Night in. Night out.

The possibility occurred to him that somewhere between being persecuted in Moscow and here, his enemies had finally assassinated him. Perhaps he was really no longer alive and this was an interlude; a journey from one world to another. He wondered if heaven or hell were stations that could be reached by train. He didn't think so but, then again, many of the disillusioned comrades he had met in the kitchen had perished. One of them, Pivo, had cautioned him that they should get out at Omsk before the weather got too cold, but somehow they missed Omsk. Then, when all were sleeping, except the guard who sat alone in the cabin idly

tipping vodka into a steaming glass of sweet tea, Volodia looked out
of the train window and found a white empty world bathed in
moonlight. Volodia had never seen anything quite like it before.
There were no monstrous concrete mountains looming out of the
darkness, no giant statues of the enemy reaching to the stars, no
lights illuminating shops or kiosks, no furry armies of humans
emerging out of the depths of the heated underworld. Nothing,
except white nothingness covered in white trees. It wasn't at all like
Moscow.

It grew colder in the kitchen and his companions began to
drop like flies. Only Volodia and Pivo had hidden in the box and
they watched helplessly as their comrades lay flat on their backs,
legs frozen mid-air, waiting to be swept into the wintry wasteland.
So many of his dead companions had been thrown out of the huge
man-made snake into the snow fields that there were now corpses
where there should have been lines. Maybe he really was sitting in
the bowels of a serpent chucketing along corpses to a dead-end.
Even Pivo had disappeared since the cabbages had attacked them.

No, Volodia couldn't possibly be dead. He felt nauseous. He
wasn't sure whether it was fear of life or fear of death or the mangy
cabbages which were causing it, but he decided that he must be
alive because he had never seen a corpse vomit.

Chuckety-chuck. Chuckety-chuck.

He must be going to a better world at the end of the line.
Wherever, whatever, however it was, it couldn't be worse than
Moscow. Only when the snows began to melt would the full horror
of his bloody persecution be exposed. It wasn't just Volodia, but the
whole of his species was suffering. Since the sudden mysterious
appearance of lethal toxic weapons, the dark city had become a
living nightmare.

When the fatal weapon first appeared in the apartment at
Preobrazhenskaya Ploshad', Volodia didn't know what it was . He
thought that it was a new kind of air-freshener which would smell
of dead flowers and foul up the stuffy air, but he deduced that as it
wasn't edible and was put away in the cupboard with an antique
bar of soap, it wasn't important. In those days, Volodia had not yet
understood that everyone wanted to kill him. He'd lived in the
fifth-floor apartment since he'd met Anya, a voluptuous female who
had chased him all around the apartment block. Eventually, on the
third floor, he had surrendered himself to her persistent charms.
They planned to move into 303 as it wasn't so crowded – just an old

crinkly pair, bent double who would croak at each other and continuously empty their purses and count out kopecks. But there were two major problems with 303: one was that there was never much food in the place and Volodia and his family-on-the-way would have starved. The other was that they had a dog. Admittedly, it was as ancient and decrepit as its owners, but dogs are dogs.

So they had decided to move into 503 just as their twelve or thirteen children were beginning to scramble out into the horrifically overcrowded world. But, in those days, they endured the hardships of communal living with a generation of humans in a three-room apartment because they thought they were safe. From the top of the pale blue pantry, Volodia and his family put up with the moans of the women as they cursed the empty shelves in the shops and the queues and the prices, and they joined in with the men as they drank vodka into the early hours of the morning and slammed their glasses onto the tables and sang songs: *Kalinka. . . Kalinka. . . Kalinka moya.*

One night, there had even been a knock at the door and the old grandad was taken away by three sombre men dressed in black. After he'd gone, a deadly hush fell into the apartment and no one spoke, as if they were scared of speaking . But Volodia heard their stifled cries in the night. He didn't know what had happened to the old grandad but he never came back which gave them a bit more space even if the event had ruined their night.

The other two humans taught at a university. Fortunately, this didn't allow them many luxuries, and Volodia and his family were spared the horrors of any nasty detergents or smelly soaps or powders polluting their favourite dining areas and seriously damaging their health. Unfortunately, this also meant that there was never any toilet paper. Although Volodia had heard that almost all humans had forgotten what toilet paper looked like by then, and were already used to wiping their arses with the *Truth*. The carefully cut square pieces of newspaper weren't as tasty as the real stuff, but Volodia stoically swallowed his dignity together with the *Truth* and said nothing.

Sasha was an English teacher, and everyday there was an influx of students tramping across the dusty wooden floor, proudly reciting to each other the wonderful achievements of the workers of their great union, a sing-song of boasts as long as the iron road itself, heaven bound, each sleeper a step nearer the red millennium.

In such a way Volodia and his family became versed in

English, both spoken and written as they would masticate over the textbooks at night, unaware that these hard covers containing great recitations of steel production and pictures of tanned healthy smiling workers would one day be accomplices to their violent deaths.

But for a long time, despite the knowledge of the mysterious can of dead flowers and their cramped and toilet-paperless lives, they all managed to exist in relative harmony. Volodia and Anya spent many memorable hours gathered round the pedestal of the samovar, climbing into the leftover cups and drinking tea and eating the crumbs of *pirogi*. Occasionally they left the kitchen and climbed into the television when it started talking to itself from the big room, or they would race along the keys of the old piano and try to play *Kalinka. . . Kalink. . . .Kalinka moya. . .* Admittedly, with only limited success.

Sasha sometimes even left the dirty dinner plates in the sink overnight which made a change from the English texts and allowed them to feast on the clogged up drain. There were certain things they knew not to do . For example, they knew not to go out in daylight and not to eat the nice, sweet sticky stuff in the jar as it was almost impossible to extricate yourself before it incarcerated you in its jelly-like claws. And if you ventured into the bedroom and one of the humans woke up, there might be a scene. But, other than that, all was well, for a while. Until signs of discontent in the humans' great union of workers began to spill into the living room as angry marches, raised voices and the sound of gunfire boomed out of the television. Until the humans smelled betrayal and no longer knew who the real enemies were or at whom to point the blame. Until that fatal eve when they had come home in the middle of the night with their forefingers hanging limply at their sides and walked into the kitchen, found something to point at, and changed everything.

Volodia sighed as the memory of the murder of his family turned the nausea into tears which involuntarily spewed out of his eyes and soaked the box beneath his legs. Volodia and his family had been sitting under or near the great silver samovar when he had heard the door slam and instantly the room was flooded in a deathly fluorescent light. His eyes had met the four flying-saucer eyes which spun around furiously in the enemies' heads, silently communicating a profane and final message.

"The devil take me. . . !"

Volodia quickly exuded his pungent juices as both a warning

and reply and leapt out of the cup, off the table, and behind the cooker. He glimpsed Sasha opening the cupboard and taking out the can of air-freshener, and felt indignant. But he was in no position to denounce the humans as within a split second they had become inhuman and were slaughtering his family, systematically, in cold, implacable blood. Volodia prayed that at least some of them had heeded his redolent warning but it was then he began to hear the hissing spray of the air-freshener and realized that its fumes were fatal. This was not the smell of dead flowers but the sweet smell of death. Interspersed between the asphyxiating attacks, he could hear the beatings and stompings of boots and English textbooks crushing heads and limbs in a manic frenzy. It would seem that his children had neither smelt his fear, nor seen the murderous red crack in the humans' spinning eyes. They had stood there, bewildered, until they were no longer shocked or horrified but dead.

"That'll teach the bastards," he heard the man say to his wife, "we've shared our lives long enough with vermin."

The murderers went off to bed but a few minutes later the man woke up screaming when he felt something crawling over his face. It was his wife's hair.

Volodia paid little attention to the cries of the human as he sat listening to the groans and death throes of his own family. When all fell quiet, he crawled out tentatively to be greeted by the crushed and desiccated corpses of his flesh and blood, flat on their backs, legs broken and frozen mid-air.

Choking on his grief, Volodia took one final look at the remains of his children, kissed the leftover pieces of Anya's cold mouth and said goodbye to peace, harmony and the old way of understanding. In a rare moment of intrepidity, he silently declared war on the enemy and vowed to avenge the deaths of his family. Then he slowly ran away from them and crawled under the door into the dark, bare corridors and took refuge in the rubbish chute. There, he crawled into a half-empty vodka bottle and promptly proceeded to drown his sorrows in diluted gasoline.

As darkness turned to grey, he was out and about in the cold, hostile white terraces of Moscow, crying and howling. He became convinced that his enemies were after him. Even the internal fire tried to burn his heart while the snow tried to freeze his legs. Fat, dirty, ugly humans with anaemic faces and big noses poking out of their clothes chased him out of boxes, out of shops, out of kiosks. They were all shouting at him, trying to beat him and stamp on him.

Volodia ran and ran, not caring where to.

Days later he woke up on a marble floor with a fellow creature clambering over his face. The stranger informed him that he was in a train station and asked if he would like to join the Revolutionaries. Volodia blinked blankly until the 'comrade' explained that there were many other homeless and persecuted comrades like himself. Creatures who had been forced to flee their homes because of the murderous weapons the humans had created. Fear and anger had caused a mass exodus to the stations and many indignant migrations to other habitations. Volodia immediately agreed to join and he was taught how to cause the humans maximum damage with as little risk to himself as possible.

The enemy who lived there were either crippled, drunk or dying; blindly holding onto icons and placards advertising poverty, begging for kopecks. Volodia learnt to excrete on their food packages and to eat their clothes while they were asleep. But his favourite trick was to climb onto their faces and exude his pungent juices into their gaping orifices. Every time Volodia did this he thought of his murdered family and laughed gleefully.

However, these were the only joyful moments. The daytimes were dangerous. Every so often, an icon would be thrown at him or the enemy would try and squash him with a placard and there was little Volodia could do but hide. The station seemed to encompass the entire city and the sky above was painted with images of hammers and sickles, blond-haired women gathering stacks of wheat and muscled men charging across the sky, waving their guns at the crystal chandeliers which hung overhead. His comrades had told him that they were the enemy who had built the union and Volodia wondered why they looked completely different to the ones who pushed and shoved through the station. There was also a little human face with beady eyes, a moustache and a short beard looking down from the wall. His eyes looked startled by what he saw. He was the one, allegedly, who had founded the great union of workers with promises of peace, freshly baked bread and tower blocks. Volodia was also told that the mosaic face had the same name as his which had secretly pleased him. But aside from learning various facts and tactics, the Revolutionaries turned out to be badly organized and most of them just ran around procreating and getting drunk. They liked to talk, but despite their promise of a better and fairer world, Volodia lived in fear.

Then one day, as he was being chased by a brush, he sneakily dived up an enemy's trouser leg. The owner of the leg screamed, kicked an imaginary football and sent Volodia flying onto a train - just as it pulled out of the station, waved off by hundreds of red, valedictory handkerchiefs. Volodia sat there for a moment and thought that, perhaps, instead of sacrificing himself in a revolution for a better world, he might find one at the next station. Then he'd watched the colossal furry Russian enemies diminish in size, until he was satisfied that they were no bigger than he was, before crawling under a door. He found himself on a rim of a toilet which had seemed a perfectly respectable place to be until the Siberian winds began to creep underneath and roar at him through the black hole, trying to kill him with their fingers of ice.

Chuckety-chuck. Chuckety-chuck.

A young woman dressed up like an old hen clucked about the train's narrow kitchen, muttering to herself in Russian. Volodia tensed up inside the box and wished he was back in the toilet. She had been the one who had tried to batter him with a dead fish and then sworn profusely because she had whacked its head off and fish was on the menu that night. A carriage door was opened and for a brief moment the chuckety-chucking was amplified and the howling wind barged in and coughed up swirling ice flakes. Then the door slammed shut and an older woman appeared in the narrow kitchen.

"Oh there you are!" the younger one said irritably. She took out a couple of cabbages from the box and piled them onto the older woman who dropped one. The cabbage rolled dangerously near Volodia who flattened himself against the side of the box and closed his eyes. If she came any closer, he would probably end up the same way as the cabbages.

"Careful Granny! We've only got this box left. There's no fish. No meat. Not even any bread. Hardly any vegetables. And only a drop of cream. We'll starve!"

Granny shrugged and picked up the cabbage. "So," she said. "What's special about that?"

"Well, at least we've got champagne and caviar for those in soft class and ourselves," the younger woman consoled herself. "My God. Look at this!" She lifted up another cabbage from the box and found it half eaten.

"Be thankful there's that much," the old woman muttered.

"I don't know how the bastards can survive in these temperatures."

"Why not? We can."

The two women began to make two big pots of *shchi*. Volodia prayed that no one would come near the box again. Light now drifted in and he could feel the women shuffling about and see the odd knife being brandished above his head. If they took one more cabbage, they would find him. Fortunately, the women seemed to have lost interest in the whereabouts of Volodia, and he was somewhat assuaged by the heat generated in the kitchen and the sound of the bubbling pot of cabbage soup. He vaguely wondered where the champagne and caviar were.

A third woman came into the kitchen, carrying a tray of cutlery and wearing bright blue mascara with pink golf balls on her cheeks and a black and white checked apron. She slammed the tray down on a shelf just above the box of cabbages.

"*Bozhe moi!* The restaurant's full already! Thank God, we're nearly there. It smells in here!" The waitress held onto her nose.

"And what am I supposed to do about it?" the young woman asked. "It's those mangy cabbages."

"And what do we have today, Zoyenka?" she asked the young woman.

"*Shchi.*"

"And what?"

"Nothing."

"Nothing. Well, that's good."

Volodia, not wanting to risk life in the box any longer, waited until he was sure no one was looking, then ran up the wall and dived onto the tray. He buried himself under a pile of serviettes while the waitress collected an army of salt pots and marched them onto the tray which was then transferred to a serving hatch leading from the kitchen into the restaurant.

The restaurant was indeed full, mainly of men who sat and drank vodka. Some were engrossed in a game of chess, some played cards while others gazed at the white trees which dawdled past the dirty windows like exhausted soldiers.

Chuckety-chuck. Chuckety-chuck.

Volodia and his tray were deposited on a table where there was a rather strange couple. He peered out of his serviette and saw a young, blonde female enemy and a dark-haired male both wearing peculiar clothes and jewellery. Volodia crept out of the serviette and climbed under the table for a closer look. One was wearing dark green jeans and big leather boots with yellow stitching around; while the other wore black leather trousers, a silver buckled belt and chunky black boots halfway up his calves.

"Excuse me, can we order?" the female asked in English, her bracelets jingling as she lifted her arm from the menu.

Volodia pricked up his ears as he heard the language, whose text had murdered his family.

"*Podozhdite minutku,*" the waitress said and walked to another table.

"What did she mean, Mark?" the female asked. Mark didn't answer.

"Excuse me!" she asked again when the waitress came close.

"*Podozhdite!*" exclaimed the waitress impatiently.

"I reckon that means, fuck off and die," decided Mark.

"*Nu i chto vy xotite?*" the waitress came and scowled at them.

"Have you chicken?"

"*N-yet,*" she replied.

"Kolbasa?"

"*N-yet.*"

"Salad?"

"*N-yet.*"

"Bread?"

"*N-yet.*"

"Well, what have you got then?"

"*Shchi.*"

The two foreigners settled for the mangy cabbage soup which they looked at in disgust before picking up spoons and tasting it. Volodia left the table and scrabbled up the back of the chair behind Mark with his eyes half-closed, desperately trying not to fall off. Despite the opacity of dirt which spread from the floors to the windows, a pale sun tried to penetrate, creating slow moving beams of smoke which hurt his eyes. As Volodia reached the top of the seat and the windowsill, he knew he was in danger of being exposed but the humans had their big noses in the soup. He noticed that the female had a silver hoop through her nostril and her hair reminded him of hundreds of rats' tails strung from her head. He shivered and turned his attention to the window, drank the condensation and was greeted by dazzling white nothingness. The brightness made him close his eyes and he quickly wobbled back onto the top of the seat, wondering if the white wilderness was really heaven or hell. Even the trees had marched away.

"Yuck! What's this!" the female cried, fishing out something long and black from her soup.

"Dunno. Wouldn't eat it though!"

Volodia felt nauseous again as he recognised Pivo's leg. He must have been in the box all the time, murdered by the aggressive cabbages. Volodia slowly crawled down to the floor, and stood among cigarette carcasses, and found himself covered in ash as the enemy showered the dead bits of a cigarette onto him. The waitress came over to the table to bring the bill. He noticed that she had holes in her stockings.

"What's this?" the foreigners asked pointing to Pivo.

The waitress shrugged her shoulders indifferently and muttered something about vitamins. "You pay dollar?" she asked in English.

"*Nyet*. Rubles. How much?'"

"*Dvadtsat rublei.*"

The waitress sighed before writing it down, muttering something about a few dollars wasn't much to ask while the foreigners opened their purses, swearing that they were being ripped off – twenty rubles for two bits of cabbage and food poisoning. Volodia hoped that Pivo had poisoned them.

The two foreigners left for their compartment, walking past two horsemen who galloped along the bleak white deserts, leaving behind them a trail of snowy cloud. Meanwhile, Volodia almost drowned in the remains of their soup trying to find the rest of Pivo but someone else must have had him. He was still clinging desperately onto the serviette when he was chucked into a black rubbish bag where he discovered the champagne bottles and tins of caviar. Just as he decided life was looking up, he found that they were empty. The enemy dumped the rubbish bag back into the kitchen and Volodia was tied up with the sloppy, over-boiled leftovers which slid down the sides of the plastic as the train passed though a great wall and sped towards Beijing.

Chuckety-chuck. Chuckety-chuck. Chuck. Chuck. Chuck.

There was a loud screeching of brakes and clunking of iron as the train ground to a halt at its final destination. It heaved a sigh of relief and refused to move another inch. Whistles were blown and all along its body, doors opened and people clambered out. The platform reverberated with the noise of thousands of humans shouting at each other, stomping their boots up and down and throwing their bags around.

Volodia was chucked out of the train together with champagne bottles and dirty serviettes. One of the green glass bottles hit him on the head. Slightly dazed, he started to gnaw his way out of the plastic bag and immediately began to race along the platform. Petrified, he scuttled past strange people dressed in blue and green, who were squatting on their haunches. They spat at him as he sped past. If this was the end of the world, Volodia was not impressed. There were twice as many enemies here as there were in Moscow. He ran onto another platform. A group of green giants came trampling towards him in trousers which hung off them and caps which almost drowned their heads, propped up only by dark glasses. One of them opened his mouth and in doing so revealed sinister gold fangs. Volodia screeched to a halt, about-turned, and recognised the leather trousers of one of the foreigners. Mark put his luggage on the floor and took out a book. Afraid that yet another English text was going to change his life, Volodia scrabbled head first into the open backpack. Seconds later, the backpack was zipped up and he found himself jolting about on the enemy's back from where he could just about peep out between the gaps of a pair of broken zig-zagging dentures.

The foreigners walked down the platform past the soldiers, one in front of the other, in a sulky silence. Volodia was in Mark's backpack which charged ahead, knocking him from his perch, and then stopped. As Volodia climbed back on top of some socks which smelt worse than he did, he could just see the one with blond rats' tails, hobbling behind, silently cursing the figure in front of her.

"Will you hurry up Ann!"

"Oh, shut up."

They boarded a train together with a thousand Chinese and sat squashed on hard seats between women with sacks of rice, and men who sat and smoked and drank beer, and wooden boxes of chickens that blocked the aisles. Volodia was put with the children in the luggage compartments and shrank back in horror from their narrow, serious eyes and accusing fingers. Everyone stared at the foreigners very suspiciously, wondering what they were doing on the train.

"Told you, we should've flown," Mark said grumpily.

"Yes, you should've done," Ann agreed.

Chuck-chuck-chuck-chuck-chuck-chuck-chuck.

They sat in silent vacuums in a compartment of noise. Volodia tried to look out of the window, but the vast beauty of China could only be seen through a smudge on the glass where a grubby hand had idly doodled and a mother had smacked it, and rubbed away all traces of evidence. All around them people were cracking nuts onto the seats, peeling hard-boiled eggs and spitting out bits they didn't want, talking, smoking and drinking or staring into space. Volodia gave up squinting at the jagged mountains and sat quietly.

"I'm hungry. Have you got any biscuits?" Ann asked.

"No."

"Can I have a look at the travel book?"

"Oh, Ann, it's put away in my backpack. I'll get it out later."

They travelled the rest of the way in silence.

From the train, Volodia was transferred to a boat where the enemy promptly fell asleep on the floor. He was beginning to feel, and not just reek of, the effects of thousands of kilometres. He tried to amuse himself in the swaying bag. He found a radio and during the night, Ann heard Tchaikovsky playing and shouted at Mark.

Volodia peered out and watched as she turned over and muttered something but he was fast asleep, his lips turned down and slightly apart. He wanted to crawl out and climb over his face and do as the Revolutionaries had taught him to do. But he couldn't get out. He laughed when Ann thumped Mark anyway, making him grunt and turn over in his sleeping-bag.

Chug-chug-chug-chug-chug-chug.

Volodia was still laughing with his mouth full of chocolate when Ann awoke. The engines had been shut off and people were preparing to disembark. She shook Mark and they silently rolled up their sleeping-bags. As he was bundled outside Volodia was greeted by an undulating mass of sea which made his head spin. It was a cold, grey morning and the clouds hung miserably in the sky and spat on them. Mark and Ann trudged into a building with their backpacks. Volodia held his breath as the zip was undone and an official hand rummaged through the bag but the socks must have saved his life as he was soon safe and zipped up.

"This is more like it!" said Mark, smiling for the first time since they had arrived in Beijing. He put his arm around Ann and kissed her.

Chuckety-chuckety-chuckety-chuckety-chuckety.

While Mark's lips were touching Ann's, Volodia was still eating his chocolate biscuits. He seemed to have been interned for ever and was even beginning to regret his hasty flight from Russia. He was bored and lonely. The only company he had were a few books, numerous articles of clothing, the radio and a packet of chocolate biscuits but only one was left as he had eaten the rest. He had never tasted anything quite like those chocolate biscuits. They didn't make them like that in Moscow. The clothes weren't very interesting but, in memory of Pivo, he had made suitable use of them and he had half-read the books. One in particular tasted familiar but he couldn't think what it was. The radio would only play Tchaikovsky, which eventually made him feel homesick. Rice, Volodia remembered, the book had tasted of rice.

Volodia was exhausted and fought his body against nodding to the great symphony of the train. His eyes closed, lulled by the galloping serpent which flew through mountains and bridged gaping chasms. He warned himself that whatever happened, he must stay awake until he got to wherever he was going. Climbing back into the packet of chocolate biscuits, he began to munch determinedly, and with his jaws still chomping, fell fast asleep.

It wasn't long before Volodia dreamt that he was being tossed about like a flea. The enemy was all around him, jostling him, trying to catch him. He could hear strange electronic sounds, various little jingles and a dribble of nasal phonetics: *mananaku, mamanku, niban sen ni densha ga mairimasu. . .* A giant human hand came towards him. Volodia screamed but the hand missed him and picked up a book. Then he heard the foreign voices and realized that he hadn't been dreaming.

"I told you to get the book out earlier. You're so disorganised." Ann complained.

"Shit!"

"What now?"

"Look at this! Something's half-eaten my book!"

The hand once again went for Volodia, only this time the hand didn't miss him. He heard Mark let out a murderous scream and try to shake his hand off, flinging Volodia out into the cold night. He scuttled off in the opposite direction but the enemy was still after him. They were throwing fireworks at him. The streets were ablaze. He dodged the bombs that were exploding in front of him and turned round and scuttled off the other way. But everywhere was the same. He looked up and saw that the sky was on fire. He was about to die at the hands of a suicidal pyromaniac. He spotted a drain and skidded into it to be greeted by twenty cautious eyes staring at him in astonishment.

"*Daijobu desu ka?*" one of them asked.

"*Chto?*"

"American?"

"Russian," replied Volodia, wondering where the hell he was and why these creatures were quite unconcerned about the fact that they were all about to die.

"Japan first time?"another asked quietly.

"Let's Get Outta Here"

Jeremy Sheldon

Jeremy Sheldon was born in 1971 and lives in West London with his fish, Jean-Luc and James T. He has been a house DJ for FISHTANK since 1992 and is currently finishing *Adeva*, a novel about sex, drugs and UFOs.

There are two types of people in this world.

There are those that lay around on the floor as children and imagined what it would have been like if we all lived upside-down. And plainly there are those that didn't. Either you were the sort of person who imagined a scenario where everyone had huge lights coming out of the floor of their living rooms – or you weren't. Take *me*, for instance. I spent many an afternoon lying in the path of one dusty sunbeam or other, imagining everyone having floor-level windows and staircase-shaped ceilings. But my wife on the other hand (my *ex*-wife, actually) didn't. Never had. Never thought she might. End of story.

Not much else in life is like that. For instance: some people like football. Love it. Absolutely crazy for it. They go starry-eyed over memories of ruddy-faced men with perms and sideburns, can tell you the winners of the League Cup in 1962 and 1985 (Norwich City, both years) and drink their tea out of a 'lucky Bobby Moore mug' every Saturday morning for twenty seasons.

Then there are those that hate The Beautiful Game. Loathe it. Won't let you talk about it at the dinner-table and you end up reading your weekly copy of *A Game of Two Halves* while you smoke your fags in 'their' garden. My *ex*-wife was – and to the best of my knowledge still is – *exactly* that kind of person. To be fair, she grew up having a couple of fanatical Port Vale fans as parents (a vale of serious tears by anyone's standards) and it should have come as no surprise that she spent the next six years and three months doing anything she could to sabotage my viewing of *Match of the Day* as well as other sundry sporting highlights. Tickets to abysmal plays, her mother, her birthday or an anniversary every so often, candlelight dinners ("we always eat in front of the telly, I thought it would make a nice change."), tropical underwear, cans of whipped cream and going into labour were all some of the diversionary tactics employed over that long and arduous campaign. She even tried going into labour a second time, one midweek evening a few years after her previous attempt. Even now, I can still summon up the memory of the satisfied look that glittered in her eyes as she breathed deeply and told me that *it was time* through increasingly clenched teeth. Luckily, the gods knew the truth, saw what she was up to and all the cup-ties were rained off that night. Furthermore, I'd learnt my lesson by then and had a pocket radio for hospital waiting-rooms, visits to dying aunts, school reunions (hers) and other eventualities. I kept it in the greenhouse and checked its batteries every Saturday afternoon between three and five o'clock.

Of course there are also all the other types of people as well. People who "don't mind" football, people who "catch the odd game after the news," who watch the Cup Final with their family each summer the same way they sit down to the Queen's Speech every Christmas. And there are people who simply couldn't care either way. The world is not, by any frantic tugging on the apron-strings of the imagination, simply divided into those who know where they were when Gazza cried and those who cry when you try to put his framed picture up in the lounge. Football, unlike staring at the ceiling with a puzzled look on your face, is something that one *can* be neutral toward.

*

It was armed with these awarenesses and my pocket radio (I'd 'won' it by saving the cigarette coupons from all the *al fresco* cigarettes I'd smoked during the first three years of my marriage) that I recently travelled to California to catch up with friends and relatives. I was to stay at my cousin's bungalow out in Belmont, a few miles south of San Francisco. The house sat on a hill, amongst groves of eucalyptus trees. According to my mother who had stayed there the previous summer, it was a paradise under unbroken skies, a sun-drenched utopia where crazy deer were known to crap into your swimming-pool or jump out at your car at STOP signs.

Let me tell you now. Never miss Maddy Friggers' talkshow on KCUF at 10 a.m. Pacific time. I also recommend the luscious Maria, star of the eponymously titled *Maria!*, who lost me early on in each episode with her volcanic Spanish, but quickly won my heart with her tartan trouser-suits and her passionate discussions on *Jovenes Alcoholicos* and *Allegados a los Famosos*. You see, I'd spend the morning sitting by the pool watching cable, trying out fruit-juice combinations, eating bags of *chips* until lunchtime before retreating inside to eat watermelon in front of MTV for the rest of the day. By Friday of the first week, things had escalated. I was up to six bags of chilli-flavoured Yam Slices with my talkshows and spent my afternoon contemplating life, the tailoring on Maria's white blouses, and the ceiling over a few microbrews. Of course, if you haven't guessed already, this was one of my most recent reveries with regard to the whole 'inverted floor conundrum' – except that something different happened this time. There I was, lying on the polished floorboards, spilling beer and cigarette ash all over my T-shirt and imagining the ladders I would need to get socks out of some notional chest of drawers that I'd stuck into the corner of the roof when I suddenly remembered something that I'd never mentioned to anyone in my life.

Top Cat.

Do you remember? He lived in an alleyway on the wrong side of town, had a gang and a great signature tune, harassed a poor police officer named Dibble and generally lived it up. After a few verses of *Top Cat! – ta tant ta ta ta – the most incredible leader of the pack...*, I tried to remember the names of the rest of TC's gang other than Choo-Choo, Spike and the regrettable Benny – couldn't – and ended up being reminded of another thing that used to puzzle me. You see, at the very end of every episode, TC used to hang up his snazzy purple waistcoat and hat, put on his polka-dot pyjamas, pop in his ear-plugs, put up his television aerial for some late-night NFL action and climb wearily into his garbage-bin / bed / office / studio-apartment – only to be helplessly whisked away by a huge truck to some ghastly refuse site of the imagination. Every epsiode this went on, and what always used to worry me was how TC got back to the alleyway for the beginning of each episode. Did he jump out the back and if so, did he drag his bin with him? Or did he ring Benny, Choo-Choo and Spike (with his *Droopy Dog* eyes) and all the others and order them to come and get him? Similarly, when Fred got locked out of the house by his sabre-toothed pussycat at the end of every episode of *The Flintstones*, did he resign himself to night's sleep on the rock-hard doorstep? Was there a back door he could resort to? Didn't Wilma get pissed off with the regular-as-clockwork cries of "WILMAAAAAA...!" every evening as she applied her curlers and prehistoric mud-pack? I was later to find out that at least in this instance, popular consensus has Wilma open the door, while only one person believed that Fred started his next sunny day in Bedrock cruelly unshaven and bleary-eyed on the Flintstone doorstep.

After a few hours, I got up, fixed myself an iced tea and scanned the television pages for any rogue episodes of either cartoon, but found neither. If I'd wanted to, I could have watched four *Creature from the Black Lagoon* films all in a row – but I'd seen them the day before. So instead, I started preparing a salad and waited for Stephanie to come down from the city.

*

"Wilma let him in."

"You reckon?"

"*Totally*."

Steph had taken another spoonful of *Fuzzy Munch*, had dipped her spoon into the tub of *Furry Slop Pops* and put it into her mouth, one hand under her chin to catch the drops. The air in the kitchen had been warm and tangy.

"And that's your last answer?"

"Yup!" Little did I know then that she would be the first of many people who believed as much.

"I think. . ." I reached for the chopped-hazelnuts sprinkler to good dramatic effect, "I think that if anything happened – and that's not to say that I'm convinced as to what *did* happen – then she left him on the doorstep. For the whole night. On purpose."

"Oh, come on Jeremy!" A few beers never did any harm to Steph's sense of indignation.

"I mean it. Pass me the crushed biscuit topping, can you."

She'd slid across the table saloon-style, knowing that only my American relations are allowed to call me *Jeremy* just as I never, ever, ever use the word *cookie*.

"Almost every show had Fred and Barney screwing things up. Betty and Wilma always saved their asses. . . "

". . . Betty and Wilma fucked up too. I can think of plenty of their scams that went wrong."

Steph had put down her ice-cream and was already reaching for the phone.

"We'll call Jackie. See what *she* says."

As it turned out, Jackie (Steph's sister) was at an architect's dinner downtown, at a Hospitality Centre somewhere on Van Ness. And although the ringer on her cellular phone had been turned down to SOOTHE mode, it hadn't been turned off entirely and we might as well have gone right in there and played the drums.

"Waddya mean 'What happened to Fred at the end of *The Flintstones?* Do you know what you've done? My phone just went off in the middle of Jay Szymanski's speech! In front of two hundred architects!" All this said in a whisper. So to speak.

I later discovered, after an intimate conversation with a beautiful attorney called Alexis Vanek, that Jackie had been obliged to frantically empty her whole handbag on to the floor in her haste to find her bleeping phone. Jan Szymanski, acclaimed designer of both Rosenfeld Memorial Museums (Chicago and New York) and guest speaker for the Civic Space Commission that evening, had been in the middle of the word *psychogeography* at the time and probably wouldn't have blinked an eyelid if Jackie hadn't managed to spill two bottles of wine over the Curator of the Powers Institute and a visiting Chief of Police, invoking the attentions of a SWAT team of waiters nearby.

Steph had elected to do the dialling while I got the talking part of the plan so I quickly ran through the problem. There was a moment's silence at the other end of the line if you didn't count the scurrying of waiters nor the faltering speech echoing in the background.

"Wilma let him in. Of course she did. Now can I please hang up?"

I put the phone down. Steph was already stretched out on a sofa with a bottle of Chablis and looking at the ceiling.

"I told you so."

Indeed she had.

"Steph? When you were a kid, did you ever stare up at the ceiling and. . . "

*

Over the weekend and the next week, I searched the newspapers for a glimpse of Fred or TC, something to jump start my memory, but they didn't seem to be showing either cartoon in that part of the state. That left me with only raw human data. I asked almost everyone I met what they thought, as long as it didn't seem obvious that the person in question would be offended. Steph, being a few years younger than me, couldn't remember the end of *Top Cat;* but claimed she did remember that at the end of every show she'd had to turn over quickly to catch the end of *Mission Impossible* because they'd clashed by twenty minutes. Jackie wouldn't budge from her position, not even under duress, and I was still undecided. A few people couldn't remember seeing or had never seen both cartoons (I asked my Aunt, my Uncle and my Grandmother next) but most had some recollection of one or the other. Even a fair number of Jackie's lawyer friends offered me ideas on the subject and were no end of fun after I brought the whole thing up one evening, in a lobster restaurant in The Embacadero. I hadn't been sure how such a line of questioning would go down; but after a few rounds of Tequila, their answers had been prolific and many of them spent the rest of the evening trying to impersonate Fred and Barney, or the giggling of Betty and Wilma, much to my and Jackie's surprise. Even the Maitre d', citing Fred's virility as his principal evidence and acknowledging that it was Wilma's *duty* to let him in, explained a theory that *Monsieur Fleentston* would have gone out for a big night of gambling and drinking with Barney and other buddies from the quarry – *non?* "A man az no ozzer course of action," he added with a smile towards Ms Vanek who was sitting next to me and whom he later escorted home, "when a woman doz no return iz lov."

In a way, it was good to know that there were other people like me out there, people troubled by the little things as well as the big. But what wasn't so great was that after a while, I was starting to get the same answers. For every gem, there were turkeys. For every "Fred went on a bender" there were five more people who gave Wilma the benefit of the doubt. Even my Aunt, after an exposition of all the salient points as presented by Steph and myself, concluded that Wilma was the key to the situation. All this said in a hushed tone you understand, with a sideways glance at my slumped Uncle who was busy watching Jerry Rice receive his millionth pass for the 49ers that quarter.

*

The results go something like this:
Ninety point four-eight percent of the people questioned in California could remember seeing *The Flintstones.* One hundred

percent of those could remember the ending (I guess shouting "WILMAAAAAA" at the top of your voice grabs the attention) and of that figure, a staggering eighty-four point two one belived that Wilma let Fred in. Of this percentage, seventy-one point eight eight percent were women. Incidentally, zero point zero two six percent of people who had seen *The Flintstones* confirmed the best of my suspicions and thought that it wasn't necessary "to find closure for that particular narrative sequence as its meaning/outcome was generically, as well as arbitrarily, convened/deferred," that there was no necessary reason to connect the credits sequence with the main body of the narrative and that the credits were *"a repeated syntagm"* anyway. As it happened, zero point zero two six percent of people who had seen *The Flintstones* was a Professor of Literature at Santa Cruz as well as being an old college friend of Steph's. And every time zero point zero two six percent got to a '/', she said the word "stroke" which I thought was pretty sexy.

The other side of the coin was a much tidier affair. Of the people questioned, exactly one third had seen *Top Cat* (twenty-three point eight one percent had seen both you see) yet only fifty percent could remember the end. The majority view: ninety point eight six percent to be exact - agreed that TC was cool. Very cool. Positively low temperature. After this, opinions varied with most – fifty-seven point one four percent - opting for the calling of the gang though zero point zero zero of these could remember any names other than Spike, Benny and Choo-Choo. The Literature Professor, now zero point zero seven one of all *Top Cat* viewers questioned, did her little bit as well and after dialling us a pizza from her bedside telephone, decided that TC was so cool that on reaching the depot, he simply had his trash-can put on the next truck back to the alley ("he was under no pressure. . . he probably had a mini-bar in his trash-can and kicked back with a highball. . . ") none the worse for the experience.

*

Start to finish, I was in California for six weeks. Enough time to learn to stop asking for "twenty Marlboro" at the fag shop, to stop calling fags *fags*, to look in the right direction when crossing the road, to know that a *Café Borgia* was the best possible way to start the day. The best thing I'd seen, or nearly seen, had been a species of Amazonian fish in the aquarium at the California Academy of Sciences. It was so brazenly vile that it was prohibited from sharing a tank with any other creatures. The little plastic sign above the tank, which had actually been empty for unspecified and wholly ominous reasons, informed that the fish had been know to attack straying cattle. Even schools of piranha were considered a soft target and after looking around at the rest of the fish and a few belligerent octopi, I reckoned *that* fact alone made it The Leader of the Pack. The Big Cheese. It was even illegal to own one in the State of California.

On my last day in America, I was still thinking about this absent fish and preparing to watch my last episode of *Maria!* – an episode about shark attack – when my Mother called.

"Is Steph there?" she asked, once I'd reassured her that I'd visited my grandmother regularly and enquired about the kids.

"No. She's at work." My Mother knew that Steph was at work, it being a Friday morning.

"That's a shame. And how are *you*? Have you packed? Are you *well*?"

I paused, looking at my suitcases stacked by the front door. The last thing I wanted on my final morning in San Francisco was another *I-never-liked-her-Are-you-feeling-better?* speech, however well intended.

"Mum?"

"Yeeess. . . ?" It is often a peculiar trait of my Mother's to sound like Bela Lugosi's front door.

"Do you remember the end of *The Flintstones*, when Fred gets locked out?"

This was a safer proposition than you might first imagine. My Mother is one of those people who, in spite of displaying many of the symptoms of prolonged parenthood, has a firm grasp of who Adam West and Burt Ward were, as well as having a healthy soft spot for the mercurial Jim Rockford. After a few minutes thinking-time, I thought of her transatlantic phone bill and suggested that she thought that Wilma simply let Fred in.

"Oh no!" she said in a tone of voice that I'd only heard her use once before. It was when I had accused her of preferring The Beatles over The Stones because she was soft. "Oh no!" she had said, "I just didn't like Mick Jagger's lips."

"Oh no!" she said down the telephone. "What I think happened was that while Fred was banging on the door, the director shouts, 'Cut!' Fred then goes back to his trailer, gets into his normal clothes and drives home. Why do you ask?

After I put the phone down, I pondered my mother's genius. That answer took some beating. A moment of pure class. Even my Professor friend couldn't have matched that. I thought about it again, thought of big ol' Fred marching back to his trailer, to his mobile phone, his cigars, a cocaine habit, an LA Rams cheerleader-or-three and all the rest. "Hey!" he would shout, "this Champagne ain't cold. Waddya all? *Amateurs?*" before steaming off the lot in his red sportscar.

Such a statement provoked questions beyond "Would Fred's feet stick out the bottom of his Buick Wildcat?" Surely it raised all sorts of issues with regard to Benny and the boys, to that stray gang of cool cats. What was the truth about Choo-Choo's pink fur and cream polo-neck? Why were Spike's eyes so droopy? How long would it be before Dibble cracked and confessed certain shocking truths about rehab (mere tabloid speculation up until then) to his Latin-American fans on *Maria!*?

That afternoon, I flew back to London. Ten hours. Non-stop. Maxine (Professor Cigliuti to you) was kind enough to take me to the airport and I'd be a liar if I said things hadn't been a little awkward as I hauled my suitcases out of the car. But after I'd given her a hug and said some nice things to her, we both cheered up and I lit a cigarette and was looking at the fading summer sky to good dramatic effect when she spoke up.

"Can I ask you something?"

"Sure. Anything you like."

"I'm embarrassed."

"Don't be."

I turned to face her and saw hesitation in the pools of her eyes.

"It's just that I wanted to know if you were being serious?"

I took one of her hands in mine. I'm a shit when it comes to conversations like this. A real shit. Even my ex-wife will agree with me there.

"Are you referring to us sleeping together. . . ? I mean. . . sort of. . . seeing. . . "

Her mouth spread wide in a smile.

"No dumbass! I meant about *The Flintstones*. And *Top Cat* too."

I replied that I had been serious.

"That's good. I'm glad. It's just that I never had a chance to ask you if you get a show called *Magnum P.I.* in England."

Magnum P.I.? I thought of Thomas, Rick, Higgins and the other TC; the magic of Hawaiian sunsets, grass skirts and a big red Ferrari. I looked at my watch. There was still thirty minutes until check-in and there was a bagel counter through glass swing-doors near to where we were standing. I hurried her over and said it was my turn to buy.

the switchback

Richard Skinner

Richard Skinner was born in 1965. He would like to thank Jim Mason and Marek Derych for their help with *the switchback*.

Jimmy Knorr woke up with a terrible hangover. He sat up and rubbed his face and shaven head. As he got out of bed and put on his jeans and T-shirt, he remembered snatches of conversation from the night before. He'd had a row with Cath and she'd walked out. He swore under his breath at her; they never seemed to stop fighting. He went downstairs and made tea and toast. While he was eating, he walked over to the window and looked out into the garden. As he suspected, he could see at least six cats dart into the bushes. He'd had enough of these cats.

Later on, he laced up his boots and went to the lock-up to work on his Mini. He struggled with the camshaft for an hour before giving up. As he walked home he swore at Cath again. When he got back, he went upstairs to his bedroom and looked out the window; the cats were still under the bushes. He took out his air-rifle from the wardrobe, found the pellets and loaded the gun. He knelt by the window, very quietly raised the sash-window, and edged the rifle out. As he aimed for the tabby, he felt his pulse quicken. He waited for a moment and then fired. The cats scattered in a flurry of activity. He reloaded the rifle and waited, at the ready.

Earlier that morning, Bert Grodzinski fed Lydia. She looked up as he spooned out the catfood and purred when he put the dish on the floor. While she was eating, Bert heard a car pull up and the horn toot. He put on his summer jacket and picked up his shopping bag and keys. He shuffled out the house to the taxi, opened the door and got in.

"*Jak sie pan miewa*?" said Barry.

"*Bardzo dobrze,*" Bert said to his brother.

Barry dropped Bert off at the post office and said he'd be

back in an hour. Bert collected his pension, and then walked slowly to the supermarket. After doing his shopping, he sat in the cafe there. He nodded to one or two people he recognised. A little before an hour later, he was waiting for Barry by the post office.

When he was dropped off home, Bert unpacked his shopping and had lunch. Lydia usually came in from outside when he arrived home, but this time she didn't. After lunch, he watched the afternoon racing on television and had a nap. It was Lydia's feeding time when he woke. In the kitchen, he spooned out some food and tapped the dish. He waited but she didn't come. He put the dish on the floor and went out into the garden, calling her name. She didn't appear. He waited for a while before going inside. As he did so, he saw his neighbour duck out of sight from an upstairs window. Bert stopped, he wasn't mistaken; he had seen the neighbour with a gun.

Bert's heart missed a beat. He went inside and checked all the rooms: Lydia wasn't anywhere. He sat at the kitchen table and held his head in his hands. He looked at his watch, 3.43; his brother would be back from his shift soon. He cleaned and tidied for an hour, then he watched television. He sat staring at the screen, thinking about his wife, Lydia. He went into the garden again and called her name, softly at first, and then more loudly. He waited to see if she would appear, but she didn't. As he turned to go back inside, Jimmy came out into his garden next door, wiping the gun. Bert stopped and watched him.

"My cat's missing and you may have shot her."

Jimmy looked up. "Me? I didn't shoot anything." He smiled.

"She's not here. Why are you shooting at cats?"

Jimmy stopped wiping the gun. "Because they were getting into the bin-bags and crapping all over the garden, that's why."

"They don't do any harm. You murderer."

"I'm no murderer and, anyway, mind your own fucking business."

Bert felt something rise from his stomach to his throat. "It *is* my business you stupid man."

"No it fucking isn't, mate." Jimmy glared at him.

Bert hobbled inside and rang his brother. He explained what had happened. "I'm certain that man next door has shot her. I hate him Barry."

Barry told him not to do anything foolish and that he would come round as soon as he could.

"I hate him Barry," said Bert, and hung up . He sat for a while longer, looking at the catflap. Lydia didn't come in. Bert put his hands to his mouth and cried.

After a long time, Bert got up and collected his jacket and keys. He went out of his house and down to the end of Oglander Street. He walked to his garage around the corner, unlocked it and went in. Closing the door behind him, he switched on the light and sat down to wait for the dusk.

He breathed heavily and tensed himself to stop the tears. The garage was quiet. He looked at his watch; 7:00. He went to the corner of the garage and picked up a can of petrol. Unscrewing the cap, he looked on his bench for a rag and, when he found one, he doused it in petrol and put it into the can. He picked up his small axe and patted his pockets; the matches were there. He carried the can of petrol and axe, switched off the light and opened the garage door. There was no one around. He closed his door, locked it and stepped across to Jimmy's garage, which was next to his. He beat the doorhandle with the axe. The sound seemed loud; he had to hit it four or five times before it gave way. There was a crunch. Bert quickly opened the door and stepped in. He could see the Mini with various parts all around. He leant forward and placed the can on the front seat. His breathing became difficult. He took out the matches, struck one and, holding the match carefully, lit the rag. He moved away, closed the door behind him and ran as quickly as he could. He heard a loud whoosh. When he stopped to look back, he could see blasts of soot around the edges of the door.

Bert Grodzinski got back home to find that Lydia had returned. She was shaking. He picked her up and sat stroking her while he waited for the police. He offered no resistance when they arrived at his house and arrested him: several witnesses had seen him running away. When asked at the station if he wanted to make a telephone call, Bert said he did, and called his brother to ask him to look after Lydia. He fully confessed in his statement to the police and was detained overnight while a charge was brought against him by Jimmy Knorr.

He was taken to a police cell where he sat on the iron bed and stared at the wall. He thought back to when he had first set fire to something. He was ten and lived in Lodz with his parents and brother. After closing up his jeweller's shop every day, his father used to arrive home and smoke a long cigar. Bert was fascinated by the flaring of the flame and, one day, stole his father's matches. He went down into the communal coal-cellar and burnt some paper. His senses quickened with the fire. He kept the matches, pleading ignorance when his father asked if he had seen them, and went out with them the next day. He saw a litter bin in the street and, as he passed by, threw a match into it. Nothing happened. He stood by, waiting for the bin to catch light, but it didn't. He looked up and down the street; a man was coming towards him. He looked back at the bin and still nothing happened, so he looked into it. At that moment, the paper in the bin caught light and flames rose into Bert's face.

The passer-by took Bert to hospital and, after cleaning Bert's face, the doctors there saw it was nothing serious: his hair and eyebrows were singed. His father arrived and left with Bert without saying a word. When they got home, his father beat him and his mother didn't speak to him for several days. That night, his brother asked him if he had been frightened. Bert looked up at him and, with tears welling, could only nod. From that day on, Bert was terrified of fire.

Barry was seven when the Germans arrived in Lodz a month later. Secrecy veiled the city. Although there were rumours of brutality and violence, life carried on as normal for the first few days of occupation. On one of those days, Bert and Barry had been given fifty *groch* each by their mother for the fairground. As they walked to the city centre, they discussed what to spend it on and decided on the switchback. When they arrived, they watched the cars rolling up and down and around high above them. The ride ended and the cars came to a halt. They quickly climbed into an empty car and pulled the metal bar over their heads. A man locked it and took their money. They waited while everyone got in and then a man waved. They started. After the first climb up, the cars turned a corner and plummeted into nowhere. Barry's stomach was left behind and he heard a rushing noise. As they climbed back up, Barry looked at Bert: he was laughing and tears were streaked across his cheeks. Barry squeezed Bert's arm. They then turned another corner and sank into nothing again.

That night, their mother was unusually busy in the kitchen. Their father sat quietly smoking his cigar. At ten o'clock, there was a knock on the door. Barry looked at Bert to ask who it could be, but he just shrugged. Their mother opened the door and their father stood up. A young, dark-haired man walked in and immediately started talking to their parents. Bert and Barry watched as their mother fetched two bags from the kitchen and handed one to each of them. She said the young man's name was Pablo and that they were to do what he said. She ushered them to the door. Barry suddenly felt alone. He looked at Bert and saw fright in his eyes. At the door, their father gave Pablo a small bundle and their mother hugged each of them, saying she loved them. Their father looked hard into their eyes and said he'd see them soon .

Pablo led them along the backstreets. They passed out of the ghetto entrance without being seen and walked quickly to the outskirts of the city. They continued and were soon walking past fields. Pablo kept his eyes on the road ahead and didn't make a sound. From time to time, he gave them some bread to eat and ate a slice himself. They walked all night. Barry was lagging behind and felt Bert's arm around his shoulder, pushing him on. Just before dawn, Pablo walked them on to a farm. They went round the back of a house and Pablo knocked on the door of one of the outbuildings. There was movement inside and then the door opened slightly. Pablo said something and they were shown in by a man in farming clothes. Barry looked around him and, dotted here and there, were about ten other children.

They stayed in the outhouse all that day, that night and the following day. Pablo left and the children were alone. The farmer came in and told them that they musn't talk. He left them hot tea and black bread. Barry kept close to Bert and slept. The following night, Pablo returned with three more children; there was a policeman with him. Bert and Barry froze at the sight of the uniform. Pablo crouched down and told them they were leaving that night in a truck and that they shouldn't be afraid. The farmer brought in more hot tea and bread and they all ate.

A truck backed up to the outhouse and, when Pablo opened the doors, Barry could see it was a Polish police truck. Pablo told the children to climb in and he shut the doors behind them. There were rough sacks and a tarpaulin in the back. Barry could see the policeman driving and Pablo changing into a police uniform as the truck pulled away. They drove all night and all the next day, through quiet country roads. The children huddled together and were quiet. Bert strained to see out the window and, once, whispered to Barry that they had just passed Bydgoszcz. They sometimes stopped in the woods during the day, when the children would get out and go to the toilet among the bushes. Bert tried to soothe him but Barry couldn't go.

After two days and nights, they suddenly stopped. All the children looked up and Barry could see Pablo and the policeman talking. Bert peered out into the night and said they were near a big town. Pablo got out and opened the back doors. He told the children to get into the sacks and not to say a word until he told them to. Bert got sacks for himself and for Barry and they climbed inside. Then the truck started again. They drove for another hour and then the truck stopped. Barry could hear voices, foreign voices, and he held his breath. The truck pulled away. After some time, it stopped once more and the doors opened. Pablo told them it was all right and the children got out of the sacks. He told them to hurry up. They climbed out and Barry could see several small boats. Pablo led them to one, where a man was waiting, and told them to get onto it. As he stepped onto the gangplank, Barry saw Pablo get out the bundle his mother had given him and hand the man some small, glittering stones.

Bert looked around the cell. He remembered when he and Barry arrived in England, they were put into a cell like this one, but only for a night. An English policeman spoke to a Polish woman the next morning, and she told them that they would travel to a farm that day where they would be looked after. The policeman handed Bert and Barry two pieces of paper. Their Christian names had been crossed out and replaced with names they couldn't read.

Two weeks after he was arrested, Bert had his court case. He was assigned legal aid and the solicitor told him that, if he pleaded guilty to criminal property damage, he would only get a suspended sentence. In the Magistrates' Court, Bert was asked how he pleaded and he said "Not guilty." The prosecution brought forward several witnesses, including Jimmy Knorr. After hearing the case for the defence, the Magistrates said they had no alternative but to find Bert guilty of criminal property damage and sentenced him to twelve months imprisonment. They recommended he serve at least six months. While his sentence was being read, Bert looked around for his brother. They looked at each other for some time, and, when he was being led away, Bert nodded to Barry.

*

At closing time, Cath waited outside the pub for the taxi. She swayed from foot to foot and breathed out hard. Her breath clouded in the cold night air. She rubbed her shaven head with her hand and then put on her hat.

Five minutes later, a black and white car pulled up. Cath got in. The driver checked she wanted to go to Oglander Street and she said yes. He stiffened and drove off. She leant back and closed her eyes; everything was spinning. She knew she had to keep herself busy, stop herself thinking about him, but she couldn't help herself.

The car was warm. She took off her hat and unbuttoned her shiny leather coat. She looked down at herself. What was so wrong with her that Jimmy didn't want her? She leant her head back and hiccuped. Never again. She gritted her teeth, then hiccuped again.

"You've got the hiccups."

Cath looked forward; the driver was looking at her in the rear-view mirror. "I know," she said.

"Would you like some tea? I have hot tea here."

He wasn't English but she couldn't tell which Eastern European country he was from. His face was soft. She leant her head back again. "No." She felt the car swerve round a corner and felt the streetlights strobe across her eyelids. She hiccuped and heard the driver answer a message on his radio. He said they were driving up the Walworth Road. Cath looked out the window to see – he was right; she had given Jimmy's address.

"Excuse me. I gave you the wrong address. Can you take me to Magnolia Street?"

The driver sighed. "Okay," he said and slowed down. He looked behind him and, after letting a car go by, did a U-turn. He radioed in his new destination. Cath wondered how much the ride would be. She hiccuped.

"Boo!"

Cath looked at the driver, who was looking back at her. She smiled. "Listen, thanks but that doesn't work, you know."

"No? It always works for me."

She gave him a glance and then leant back. She hiccupped. They drove quietly for a few minutes and then Cath felt the car slowing. She looked up but it was only a red light. Just as the taxi was stopping, it jerked to a sudden halt. Cath was thrown out of

her seat and then fell back into it. She looked at the driver who was
staring back at her in the mirror.

"Sorry, but it's for your hiccups. Have they gone?"

Cath couldn't believe it. "Look, I know you want to help me,
but just don't bother, okay? Just don't bother!" She glared at him
and he looked at the road in front. She hiccuped and felt the nausea
inside her.

The lights changed to green and the driver turned left
wordlessly. Cath looked at the streets; they were empty and wet.
She wondered why she always got the nutcase drivers. Not long
now. She began to calm down. They drove in silence for a few more
minutes before the driver spoke.

"You know what I'm going to do to stop your hiccups? I'm
going to take you into the woods and rape you." He slowed down
and stopped at another set of traffic-lights.

Cath looked at him. "What did you say?"

"I said I'm going to take you into the woods and rape you."

"You fucking creep! I've got friends who'll sort you out, you
know! I'll get the fucking skinheads onto you, scum!"

He froze. Then he turned round, lurched over the seat and
grabbed her throat. She saw the contortions on his face and her
mouth fell open. She clawed at the hands gripping her throat. His
thumbs deepened into her neck. Panic rose in her. She kicked the
seat, then kicked higher at his arms. He pushed down on her. A car
horn sounded. She kicked his arm hard, it gave slightly. She kicked
again, harder, and his arm gave way. His other arm relaxed and let
go. She scrabbled for the door handle, opened it and stumbled out.
Someone got out of the car behind and ran to her. Someone else ran
to her from the pavement. She fell in the street, holding her neck
and coughing. She couldn't breathe. There was a hand on her
shoulder which made her flinch; somebody spoke to her.
Everything was spinning and the voices were very faint to her.
Then she couldn't see or hear anything else. A man next to her
stood up and looked into the taxi. The driver was still sitting there,
his body convulsed in sobs.

Catherine de Man spent two nights in hospital suffering from
severe bruising and shock. The police took her statement and
Barry Grodzinski was charged with attempted rape. He had
offered no resistance when the police arrested him. After a police
doctor had examined Catherine, the charges against Barry

Grodzinski were changed to assault and actual bodily harm. Grodzinski was assigned the same solicitor as his brother. The case went to the Magistrates' Court where Grodzinski's solicitor cited Bert's recent sentencing as mitigating circumstances. He also went into some detail about Grodzinski's childhood traumas during the war. After hearing the case for the defence, the Magistrate found Barry Grodzinski guilty of actual bodily harm and sentenced him to six months imprisonment, of which he had to serve at least two months.

As there were no immediate relatives of the Grodzinski brothers, the police asked the Blue Cross to find a new home for Bert's cat. The Blue Cross said it was difficult to place fully-grown cats into new homes and, after a few months, they still hadn't found anywhere for Lydia. They had no alternative but to destroy her.

The Mystery of the Packet

Sophie Stewart

Sophie Stewart lives in London. She describes herself as beautiful and available.

"D'you like me new T-shirt?" asked Susie. "Me and Tracey had them printed especially."

Susie opened her jacket to reveal an undersized pink number with *Slappers Go For It* emblazoned in silver across her breasts.

"Subtle."

"Trace got it as a sympathy present for me having sex with this dwarf Australian at a party in Dalston."

"I thought you were going out with that Chinese bloke with braces."

"Nah, dumped him. I mean, he's seventeen, I'm twenty-five. It was getting embarrassing. I'm sure I only went out with him cos of grannie-bashing." Susie had worked for several months with old dears whose bums she had wiped and beards she had plucked. This had led her to start making eyes at nine-year-olds. "Besides, he couldn't get it up."

"Oh not again."

"I know." Susie threw herself down on my sofa. "I mean, what is it about me? A gel can get para, you know?"

"Not you." That was exactly what I liked about Susie – she had a kind of unshakeable self-confidence. Her mid-twenties life-crisis had lasted just one day during which she had booked herself a flight to Australia where she'd decided to train as a reflexologist ("I've always had this thing about feet"). "Funny, this sex business," I mused.

"What would you know about it, cobweb fanny?"

"Oh right, rub it in. Actually, I've given up trying to have sex this decade so I went out and bought this book on masturbation called *Sex For One: The Art of Self-Loving*'"

"Any good?"

229

"Nah. I was hoping for a thirty-second guide to instant finger high but it's all about sixties encounter groups and consciousness-raising."

"Why don't you just fuck someone?"

"That's too obvious. Anyway, I can't bear sex if it involves me. Normally I wouldn't mind but Love is in the Air at the moment. Even Cassie's got a boyfriend and before him she hadn't even got off with someone for four years."

"No wonder she's such a bleedin' zoid."

I'd actually been quite disturbed by Cassie's new amour; even if she was seeing Dave Hardcore, a guy so perverse that he'd wanted to film his ex having an abortion.

"I just don't understand how you're managing to have a boyfriend," I'd said to her the previous evening. Cassie had, for once, not been stoned and was drinking a glass of whiskey. She claimed that she was admitting her contradictions but actually her dealers were dry.

"I know, it's bizarre. It's like, I'm abnormal, fucked-up, useless – just like you – but here I am, being normal."

"Amazing."

"But I still make a point of walking naked in front of Dave in broad daylight cos I'm so convinced that he can't have realized what a mutant I am." Cass had eczema.

"Really? That's so courageous. I'm such a coward. I used to think that I was brave but actually I was just hopelessly reckless."

"You need a man to protect you."

"No, men need to be protected from me."

Susie had managed to get us guest-listed to some dodgy rave that evening where Tricky Dicky, a DJ we knew, was working. Both of us had been obsessed with Tricky for ages after meeting him at Chan's one night. He'd been fairly nondescript but seemed to sport one hell of a bulge.

"I bet he's got a stonker," Susie had said and had instantly swapped phone numbers. However, Susie's would-be romance had been interrupted by her sudden nervous breakdown and subsequent runner to Israel. And since she'd been back in London, her rampant promiscuity and grannie-bashing had left little time for blokes who were non-certs. Now, before she left for Australia, she was determined to at last solve The Mystery of the Packet.

Tricky was on the decks mixing when we arrived, smoking a spliff and chatting about football. I remarked to Susie that he'd put on a lot of weight since I'd last seen him.

"I know, rank isn't it? I'm thinking of chaining him to a radiator for a week to slim him down." Susie hated having sex with fat blokes as she said she could feel their stomachs slapping against hers. "I know I shouldn't say anything. I've decided not to have children in case they develop my fat arse. I wish there was some sort of test they could do to check."

Susie turned to Tricky. "Alright?"

"Yeah, you?"

"Fucked off. You stood me up last night."

"Sorry. I got pissed with me mates and ended up in a bowling alley in Streatham."

"Sort us out then."

We dropped some E and then danced around and had a few spliffs. It was the average casualty-city night out; making me think of some annual Narcotics Anonymous bash gone horribly wrong. The neon blue light made everyone look particularly grotesque and I remembered Lilly saying that she thought the widespread use of Ecstacy was some government plot to turn the young into imbeciles. However, as I started coming up half an hour later, I began noticing how friendly everyone was and how good the tunes were and all the boys with nice haircuts.

"I love you, Susie."

"Oh no, not again."

"No, I mean it, it's not just the drugs talking. You see, we've all got to love each other more. It's like the tune says, 'it's time to get up and get along'."

"Yeah right." Susie stared at me strangely. "You look like Keith Chegwin. Christ, everyone looks like Keith Chegwin. I better snog Tricks before it's too late."

I was left on my own on the dance floor and wiled away a couple of hours muff-chucking at any bloke who went past. Others called me a prick tease but it was just my way of saying hello. At a particularly self-obsessed stage, a bloke came up and asked me if I wanted a drink. I was thirsty and he didn't look obviously deformed, so I agreed. We chatted at the bar for a while and he told me his name was Dwayne and that he was the fifteenth child of an alcoholic Country and Western singer now dead of cirrhosis. He seemed to be my kind of bloke. It all goes a bit blurry here and I vaguely remember snogging and tooting and refusing to go home with him and then agreeing to meet for lunch the next day. Susie and I drove back in the car feeling fairly satisfied with ourselves: we'd both touched tonsils and Tricky had asked her out to a party.

Bored the next day, I decided that I would meet Dwayne for lunch. I sat in the restaurant drinking a beer and worrying that I couldn't remember what he looked like, that I had chaffing on my chin and please God let him not have a beard. Dwayne arrived a few minutes later looking equally nervous. Luckily, facial hair was not an issue. We drank and talked and he told me that he'd been a roofer until he'd fallen off a roof and broken his leg and now he worked as a photocopying assistant. I admitted to being an alcoholic barmaid who masqueraded as an arthritic dancer on her days off. It also turned out that I'd once shared a flat with his half-sister Joleen, a notoriously unsuccessful nymphomaniac. Dwayne and I ended up snogging in a gay bar in Camden Town and agreed to meet the next evening.

The following night was a whirl of horrendous parties stretching from Chelsea to Parson's Green. I saw it through a coke-induced air of calmness as I was one of the few people that toot made quieter and more sensitive. We ended up back at my place for some drunken sex. Then we lay in bed looking at each other.

"I can't believe we get on this well," said Dwayne.

"I know. I mean I always think that strangers are enemies you haven't yet met." There was a lot of hand-holding, eye-gazing and general soppiness. We agreed to meet the next evening.

Before I went out, I telephoned Susie to see how she was doing in her search for the solution to The Mystery of the Packet.

"Oh don't ask. I went to the party and it was lame. So then we all went back to Tricks and smoked smack and played Sega."

"Oh not Sega."

"Never again. I still feel severely shit. Anyway, he just got the nods and blanked out and I couldn't even have a look cos there were other people in the room. So last night I ended up at some anaesthetist's party in Barkingside hospital. I met this nurse and we made out in Casualty and then went to his place and played games with ice-boxes."

"Oh dear."

"And I've got to meet Bellbottoms tonight but how'm I gonna explain the ice-burns?" Susie sighed. "Anyway, how's it going with Ronelle?"

"Dwayne. Okay, I guess. Actually, he's alright."

"Don't do another runner, whatever you do."

"I won't." I lied.

Dwayne and I spent the evening with some dope-addict friends of his who all claimed to be musicians because they'd once picked up a guitar. It was a quiet night as, after my hol break, I was returning to dance college the next day and he was going home to nurse his quarter-horse that had just recovered from colic. We went back to my place and Dwayne commented that I was the most undomesticated girl he'd ever met.

"Have you looked in your fridge recently?" he called from the kitchen.

"I try not to."

"Well, it contains precisely one eye-mask, two carrots, a tub of lard and a packet of Rizla."

"Oh I was wondering where the Rizla were." Dwayne got into bed and we played around for a while before I took some sleeping pills.

"Why d'you need them, honey?"

"I don't sleep, really. Haven't since I was thirteen."

"I always sleep well." He curled up around me whilst I stroked his hand. I had a feeling I was doing something I shouldn't. It was nice being warm and held but. . . someone who slept well? That meant he couldn't be like me. Fuck-ups never slept well; probably because our consciences were never easy. I had made a mistake. Dwayne wasn't one of us.

I nervously broached the subject with one of the girls at work, Gerry, who was an ex-dancer and acted as my guide and general mentor.

"You're pretty fucked up, Gerry, aren't you?" Gerry always said that she'd only become a dancer because she'd been a half-caste with spots living in Essex.

"Totally." Gerry turned to one of our two customers and handed him a *Budweiser*. "Three quid."

"Three quid!"

She stared hard at him. "Got a problem with that mate?"

"Christ no." He gave Gerry a fiver and cowered away.

"Now, your boyfriend Paul, he's a bit of a state," I continued.

"Tell me about it. He's just started therapy and comes out with boring psychological revelations most nights."

"D'you think we should only go out with fuck-ups like us or would it be better for us to see normal people?"

"I dunno." Gerry walked to the side of the bar, lit a spliff and started spraying air-freshener everywhere. "I mean, my first boyfriend's now a woman called Rebecca. And then there was Darren; well, we once agreed to share sexual fantasies and mine was having two men at once so he punched me."

"What d'you reckon Tim?" I asked the other barman, who was leafing through a copy of *Tropical Fish Monthly* underneath the counter.

"Fuck knows. I once read Chekhov and he said that what women want is originality in a man; like a bloke who wears felt shoes all year round. That's why I'm still doing my fish mobiles."

"Right. . ." I downed another shooter. I was drinking too much, again. "Oh screw it, I refuse to care."

Gerry looked at me seriously.

"One day, Sophie, you're going to have to find a way of dealing with your problems other than by knocking back the vodka and going 'I refuse to care'."

I said goodbye to Susie. She was leaving for Australia.

"How's it been going?"

Susie looked down at her stuff on the floor that she was trying to cram into a tiny rucksack. "It's been a fucking nightmare. Bellbottoms tried to make me have Sunday lunch with his family yesterday and then forced me to listen to an Elvis Presley album with him."

"Oh no."

"I know. He became particularly sickening when 'Love Me Tender' started playing. Then Tricky stood me up again so I had to shag that nurse and this morning his Mum made me watch videos of her ballroom dancing in Torremolinos. I can't wait to get on that plane."

"So you never solved the Mystery of the Packet?"

"Nah . . . I'm not that bothered really. One of Tricky's mates told me he was impotent." Susie grinned. "Anyway, men, they all do a runner in the end."

"Tim at work says that all his girlfriends emigrate."

"I'm not surprised."

"But, hang on. . ." I could feel my face contorting in a rare act of thought. "Like, how can you accuse other people of doing runners when you're leaving at least three blokes who think they're going out with you to fly to Australia?"

"Oh no. See, there are two types of people: bolters and stickers. I just stick with a lot of people."

"What about me?"

Susie raised her eyebrows.

"I know. Sometimes I think I was born with no faculty for intimacy."

Dwayne returned from drenching his horse and I took him to a staff party at the club. He was happy and drunk and I was happy and trying not to get too drunk.

"He's really nice," said Gerry after meeting Dwayne.

"Yeah," agreed Tim. "Not one of your normal sleazebags. He can speak English and everything. Don't blow it, Sophie."

"What makes you think I would?"

"That shifty look in your eyes."

I watched Dwayne knocking back Tequila slammers and dancing in a peculiar manner.

"Oh, I dunno. . ."

"You need to fling," said Tim.

"What?"

"When you meet someone, you have to be brave. You have to fling yourself into their arms and sometimes they'll catch you and sometimes they'll step aside and you'll hit the floor. If they step aside, you may get bruised, but you'll get up again. But if you're caught. . . You've got to fling, Sophie, or you'll never know whether they'd have caught you or not."

Dwayne and I went to a late-night drinking bar afterwards where we smooched for a while.

"Listen," he slurred, "let's get this straight. I'll always be honest with you." *Cool*, I thought, *because I'll always be dishonest with you.* "I want you to be my girlfriend."

"Good," I said.

"I haven't got a lot of money, though. I know that bothers you."

"You talk as if I was some bloodsucking leech." He coughed. "Okay, maybe I was, but I've changed. Of course I'll go out with you. Hey, I love you."

"I love you too," he said.

"Good." We then went back to his place, where, pissed and exhausted, we both collapsed asleep.

When I woke in the morning, it all felt different. We lay hungover and dreamy with each other for a while and then I called a cab and got dressed. Something felt weird. He had found me out. He knew that I was a lunatic.

"I'll call you later," I said and kissed him and left.

I never called him. He never called me. I never flung.

Little Miss Muffet

Phil Whitaker

Phil Whitaker was born in Kent in 1966. He studied medicine at Nottingham and has worked as a doctor in Oxforshire and London. He now lives in Norfolk with his partner Lynn Franks, who works in palliative care. He gratefully acknowledges financial support from the British Academy for his MA.

Valerie Gough sat, curled sideways on the wooden box-seat in the bay window. She stared out at the garden, her gaze fixed on the rose beds. As she rocked back and forth, the wood of the seat creaked. Her nails hurt as she dug them into her palms.

She stood, a steadying hand stretched out to the window-frame. The weak morning sun glinted off a spider's web on the other side of the glass. She spotted the architect crouched in a furled-leg ball in a corner of the pane, a female *Theridion*. Valerie stared at the motionless spider, a desolation growing within her. She turned from the window and walked out of the lounge, towards the stairs.

I Stephen Harold Gough take you Valerie Jennifer Moffat to be my lawful wedded wife

The bed was unmade, duvet flung back, sheet and both pillows crumpled. The medicines lived in the bedside cabinet. Rummaging in the drawer she found: her HRT, Stephen's old blood-pressure pills, sleeping tablets, a packet of Diarret, anti-depressants, a Vicks Sinex nasal spray. She came across a white tub proclaiming *The Power To Relieve Pain Fast*. Picking this up she hurried out of the bedroom, leaving the cabinet drawer open. She hesitated at the top of the stairs, hand on banister, then turned and walked back along the landing.

In the bathroom, she tipped the toothbrushes and the Colgate out of the enamel mug on the wash-basin. The bottom of the mug was coated in a limy deposit and held half an inch of stagnant water. She rinsed it out, using a flannel as a dishcloth, working away at the enamel long after the last of the scale had gone.

Tapping the opened tub against her palm, Valerie slipped a couple of painkillers out. She ran fresh water into the cleaned mug and gulped the tablets down. For a moment, she contemplated the rest of the pills nestling together in the container. Several dozen. Jumbled visions of: her reception class terrorizing some poor supply teacher; headlines in *The Oxford Times*; Jenny and Chris holding each other, watching her coffin bump off the sides as it is lowered into a deep grave; colleagues' down-turned heads.

Sweet Jesus Val all I want is to spice things up

With a start she looked at her watch. The toothbrush-mug made a stark clink as she set it down. She looked up, meeting her own gaze in the mirror above the basin. The longer she stared, the more the face seemed to belong to someone else.

She had to concentrate hard on the stairs, not trusting her feet to land securely. It felt almost as if she didn't own them as she watched them taking one step at a time.

In the lounge again, Valerie held the phone to her ear, listening to the ringing tone. Eventually the line clicked and the school secretary answered.

"Hello Julie, it's Val. Oh, not so good. I don't know, just not feeling right. No. Could you tell David? – he'll need to get cover sorted. Yes, I'm going to try to see one this morning. Yes. Thanks Julie. Yes, I will."

The handset landed not quite squarely, bumping off the sides of the moulding as it settled. Letting out a long breath, she sat on the sofa, eyes roving over the pictures on the piano. Photos of: Jenny skiing; Chris graduating; her and Stephen in the garden; Jenny and Stephen in the garden; Stephen and Chris dressed up ready to go to a rugby international. Stephen's doctorate, proudly framed from twenty-odd years ago. She'd tried to read his thesis: 'Morphology of cytoskeletal spindles in heart muscle cells of *Xysticus lanio.*' She could remember two things: all spiders' hearts are in their abdomens not their chests; the male *Xysticus* stops its mate from killing it by fastening her to the ground with silken threads.

School taken care of, the day stretched ahead. She was alone. Picking up the address book, she flicked through the pages, trying to think of someone she could call. Chris would be on the Tube to work by now. She'd never get anyone to answer the phone in Jenny's Hall at this time of the morning. Who else? She had friends, certainly, but. . . she couldn't even begin to imagine what she would say.

month after month I've been putting up with this Val it's playing havoc with my work

She propelled herself from her seat, escaping the lounge. She felt giddy and sick, needed to get out, into fresh air. Her quilted jacket hung on a peg in the hall. She put it on, together with her best court shoes; her trainers lived in the kitchen, next to the fridge. She went out the front door, skirting round the house to the back garden. The shed padlock was hanging open. She collected her gloves, and the secateurs from their hook on the wall.

The late October sun was weakly warm. She set about cutting back the roses. The secateur blades snatched at the stems, sometimes slicing straight through, sometimes slipping, leaving a white scar. She tried to concentrate on the rhythmic snipping, pruning hard down to the lowest bud from which new life could spring next year.

An *Aranea* hung in the centre of its orb web, strung out between an Ena Harkness bush and a Montezuma. A white cross decorated its back. She could recognize the common species easily after years of Stephen's tuition. She lived an uneasy truce now with those that shared the house. Even the bath-bound *Tegenariae*, legs spreading over two or three inches, looked somehow less frightening when she knew they hadn't come up through the plumbing; had only climbed in there because they were thirsty. And late of an evening, when a male might be seen sprinting across the lounge carpet, she'd dampen her instinct to stamp on him, knowing he had only broken cover in his desperate search for a mate.

a little bitter taste in the mouth that's all I don't see why you won't millions do

A gentle gust wobbled the web. Valerie paused in her pruning, eyes searching for some fly; to see the spider run to it and inject poison, bind it in silk. Before she met Stephen she'd hated spiders. He'd changed that, as he'd changed everything, capturing her with his boyish enthusiasm: *oh no Val that's just a myth in fact the female hardly ever eats her mate – and another thing – they don't all catch things in webs you know some jump and bite their prey others spit glue and there's one called Bolas who hunts with this length of silk with a sticky ball at the end which it* swings *it actually* swings *it at insects and hauls them in and kills them with a bite - can you* believe *it Val?*

She eased the secateurs open again and grabbed blindly at another branch. The blades bit through the woody stem with a gristly snap. The orb web broke in a number of places as its support fell away. She tried to steady the branch, prevent the destruction, but it was too late.

Its web disintegrating, the *Aranea* launched itself into the air, suspended on a dragline of silk. To Valerie's eyes it seemed to be disobeying the laws of gravity, floating and swaying when it should by rights have been falling directly to the ground.

it won't hurt you to lose a bit of weight

Valerie straightened up, back aching, watching the *Aranea* clamber back up the dragline. After the spider disappeared behind some leaves, Valerie stood for a long while, looking around, listening to cars as they passed by on the other side of the fence.

Holding the secateurs loosely, she walked slowly round the perimeter of the garden, amongst the tall untamed grass which the mower could never reach. As she walked, feet swishing through the dewy strip of meadow, her eyes scoured the jostling stems. It was too late in the year, even with the unseasonable October sunshine. *Mirabilis* would be long dead and her children dispersed and grown.

Wait a mo Val that's a Mirabilis there just by your foot you can tell by the silk see how she's woven a great sphere all around those grass stems that's where she's got her babies there she is see her there's mother she'll sit right there guarding her young till the moment they hatch and set off on their tod and then that's it job done end of story she just turns up her toes and dies.

The sun dipped behind some clouds and the morning felt suddenly cold. She was getting nowhere in the garden. She walked back across the trimly kept lawn, towards the shed.

oh great Val next you're going to tell me you're mad as well as frigid

Valerie hung the secateurs on their peg, dropped her gloves back in the drawer, and closed the shed door behind her. At the back door to the house, she eased the shoes from her feet, staring at the mud streaked over the shiny leather. The metal grill pressed hard ridges into each bare foot. Her toes curled with brief discomfort.

*little miss muffet sat on her tuffet eating her curds and hey Val you
look gorge is a deep cleft in the land yourself a decent man get hitched and
live happily ever ready duracell durex cell keep going eight times longer my
god Val that was fantastic marry me*

She turned the key in the lock.

*alright Val if you think it's hormonal get yourself down to the doctor
alright Mrs Gough try taking these and come and see me again in three
month after month I've been putting up with this Val it's playing havoc with
my work and no play makes Stephen a very dull boy*

She leaned on the alloy handle and the door swung open into the
kitchen.

*a little bitter taste in the mouth that's all I don't see why you won't
millions do you know that the average ejaculate contains enough sperm to
impregnate the entire population of China Indian or Lapsang Souchong*

The note was on the kitchen table.

*support Mrs Gough have you any support now your children have
left home I think you should try and think of me a bit more Val I've been very
patient is different Mrs Gough and it may be that the pills aren't going to
work are they Val my god to think how good it used to be between you and
me Mrs Gough I think you may be better off seeing a counsellor oh great Val
next you're going to tell me you're mad as well as frigid*

Beside the note lay the envelope, opened in puzzled haste just an
hour before.

*about to cry no don't let yourself no don't let yourself go it's
important to keep yourself looking good night then Val I've got to make an
early start in the morning*

She sat at one of the chairs. Her nails dug into her palms.

*Sweet Jesus Val all I want is to spice things up a creek without a
padded bras are okay so what's wrong with wearing this sort of thing is
disgusting I look ridiculous I feel dirty magazines in his desk drawers that's
what you wear why won't you try something a little more you know now*

Chris and Jenny have left home on the range of positions is endless Val we've only ever tried two for tea and tea for two and you for me and me for you my little Miss Muffet I'll love you forever and forever love you with all my heart love you whenever we're together love you when we're apart

She smoothed out the paper, crumpled earlier in her uncomprehending hand.

I Stephen Harold Gough take you Valerie Jennifer Moffat to be my lawful wedded wife to have and to hold on a minute Val you don't have to stamp on it just trap it with a glass like this and slide a piece of card underneath see then you can put it out the door it won't hurt you to try and lose a bit of weight a mo Val that's a Mirabilis there just by your foot you can tell by the silk is sexy it turns me on to see you dressed in this kind of thing makes me feel horrible Stephen I'm nearly forty five quid that cami cost me Val you could at least try to understand Stephen I'm a middle-aged woman now not one of my students just called Val she things she's caught a rare specimen and wants me to go round and round the garden like a teddy bear one step two step tickly under there

Val puts the letter back down. She reaches for the mug of tea she barely touched that hour ago. It is stone cold. She tries to imagine seeing him again, coming back to collect his things; what they would say. Before he *swans off*, back to *her*, no more than a few years older than *Jenny*.

She slams the mug down. Tea slops on the table-top. The chair shrieks its protest as it's moved abruptly back. Walking quickly through to the lounge, Val heads straight for the piano, knocking the photos off with a single sweep of her forearm. His doctorate is the last to fall. She picks it back up and smashes the glass against the corner of the footstool. She stands, breathing heavily, then drops the frame.

Turning a half circle, Val looks about her. As she moves, one bare foot presses down on some fragments of glass. The shards sink into the deep pile of the carpet without cutting her.

She walks over to the bookcase and starts to pull his books off the shelves. In two's and three's they fall, some splaying open on the floor.

Extract from

Grace

Carrie Worrall

Carrie Worrall is currently working on a novel called Grace,which is set in Manchester where she lives with her husband and five year-old son Joe. She also writes short stories, and is working on a film adaptation of Mikhail Bulgakov's novel *Master & Margarita*, with Lisa Selvidge.

Hair Shirt

Derek opens his eyes to the sound of the toilet flush eighteen inches from his head. It is his usual alarm call. The rattle and gush of the cistern fades to a urinal hiss, which is abruptly drowned out by the drubbing of water on the shower curtain. During the next five minutes of steady running water, Derek's bladder fills. Then the shower is switched off with a complaining shudder from the pipes. He can hear the squeak of a soapy sole on enamel, and the discreet stage whisper of an aerosol being squirted twice under each arm.

Derek stretches out flat, trying to delay the urgency of his need for the bathroom, but his muscles are excited by the sounds from beyond the partition wall, and he sits up, sliding his legs round to sit on the edge of the bed, the duvet draped over his lap. He stretches his arms up and arches his back and shoulders, looking at himself in the mirrored wardrobe door. In the speckled light of morning filtered through a bamboo blind, he doesn't look bad. Hooking his right arm over his head, letting the hand flop down to his other ear, Derek twists slightly, a quarter-turn at the waist, so that his pale torso is in profile in the mirror. Pulling in his stomach, he inspects the padded underline of his ribcage. He runs his left thumb reflectively across the flattened hollow of his right armpit, the nail scraping a residue of deodorant and talc, and teasing out an odour that prompts him to lower his arm. He hears the click of the bathroom lock, the creak of the landing, and the slap of a palm on his bedroom door.

"Half-seven, Dad," shouts Christopher, on his way down the stairs.

It is Monday morning, and Chris is acting as though nothing has happened. Derek takes his turn in the bathroom, which is steamily scented with Calvin Klein shower gel and freshmint toothpaste. On summer evenings, with the frosted glass window open, he can stand here and pee looking out over the neighbours' gardens, with their bright toys, washing lines, crazy paving. Standing at the toilet with the window shut, Derek feels the bathroom crowding him. By some quirk of design or plumbing, the bath and the toilet are squashed together, while the wash-basin on the other wall seems to have more than enough space to itself. Relieving himself of a pressurized stream, Derek notices that mildew has colonized the edge of the vinyl wallpaper where it butts up to the white tiles of the windowsill. The flabby pink roses of the wallpaper look as if they have been sprinkled with black pepper.

By the time Derek emerges, his round shoulders and wide thighs blotched pink by hot water, there is a smell of charring toast rising up from the kitchen. He sniffs, imagining carbon molecules like dandelion fluff, wafting upwards on circling thermals of Radio One.

In winter, the climate of the landing through which all the warmth of the house must pass on its inevitable route to the loft, baffles Derek. Back in his renovating years, he put in the central heating himself. He persuaded a keen young firm that by drawing up plans and estimating the cost of installation they might actually win the work, then used their plans and did the job himself for half the price. He bought the materials from a plumbers' merchant who was less interested in seeing Derek's trade card than in selling him the goods, and followed a vague set of instructions in the *Reader's Digest Encyclopaedia of Home Improvement*. Then, to save a few feet of pipework and a lot of effort, he had ignored the part of the design that provided for a tiny radiator at the top of the stairs. Paring down costs to a minimum, he amputated one short limb from the system, and is still suffering the consequences. Derek suspects that the eternal draught flowing up the stairs and round the landing is a revenge on the part of the contractor whose calls he never returned.

Derek closes his bedroom door behind him. Here, the tinny strains of Christopher's radio are fainter. It is ten minutes to eight. Chris leaves at eight, and Derek wants to talk to him before he goes. He has a point to make. It is a point he should probably have made the previous evening but, too weary to stay up for Chris's return, he had put it off. But they have slipped back so easily into their familiar routine, and he finds it difficult to get a perspective on the scale of his son's transgression. Sitting on the edge of the bed to dry between his toes, Derek enumerates his son's mistakes. One: Chris failed to come home from the football match on Saturday afternoon. Two: he failed to call on Saturday evening to say when he'd be back. Three: he did not phone on Sunday morning to say where he was. Derek discovered his bed had not been slept in, and despite himself, began to worry.

From a nineteen-year-old viewpoint, Derek imagines, there is nothing to be said, no harm done. It is not as if Chris were out all night indulging in dangerous drugs or excessive drinking. But Derek had not been privy to this reassuring information, and his weekend was ruined by a few hours of irrational fear. All Sunday morning, he stayed close to the phone, telling himself he was sitting on the floor by the patio doors simply to catch the sunshine where it fell through the glass. He turned over the pages of the Sunday paper, looking for some headline that might seem more significant than the unexpected absence of his son. When the phone rang, Derek caught it before the second trill.

"Chris just told me you are thinking of selling the piano," said Eve.

"Chris?"

"No, it's Eve. You can speak to Chris in a minute if you want, but I need to talk to you about the piano. I can't believe you'd just go and sell it off. My poor mother."

Derek's anxiety gave way to an anger so heavily diluted with relief that it had no staying power. Now, in the breezy normality of Monday morning, he feels only gladness that everything is back in its place. Still Derek feels something ought to be said, and cannot decide between righteous paternal indignation and friendly fatherly concern. So he dresses in a less leisurely manner than he would like, putting on clean underpants (briefs, not boxers) and socks, choosing a plain blue shirt from the wardrobe and the dark grey woollen suit he wears for everyday days, not boardroom days. It is his oldest suit, still presentable, but slightly baggy around the knees and elbows. The cuffs are not as sharply defined as they once were, and there is a softness about the collar which suggests that the jacket has hung by the neck once too often from that stubby plastic peg behind the passenger seat of a company car. But it is comfortable, and smells reassuringly of Derek's working week: a powdery hint of Xerox toner and newly unwrapped paper, a smoky trace of coffee breaks in the Fools' Pantry, the only part of the building where smoking is permitted. Derek defers his choice of tie, and pads down the slippery carpeted stairs in his socks.

Chris is hunched over a bowl of cereal: two slices of irredeemably burned toast sit on top of the overfilled bin. At nineteen, Chris is taller than his father, and confidently nonchalant about his appearance. Today he is wearing a pair of jeans ripped across the knee, and Derek supposes, various layers of unpressed T-shirts under a voluminous mottled black and white sweater. The sweater hangs off broad shoulders, and loops down in a great bag at the back. It has seen better days. His long, nearly black hair is the same colour as his father's, but has his mother's fine texture and flyaway temperament. This morning, Chris has it bound with an elastic band, a couple of inches below his nape.

"There's no more bread," says Chris through a mouthful of muesli. "Coffee's in the pot."

"How was your weekend?" Derek asks, as he picks a mug from the draining board, shaking the water off before pouring in the coffee. He sees Chris's spoon hesitate midway between the oaty sludge in his bowl and his mouth.

"Everything okay at your Mum's?" asks Derek, calmly.

Chris mumbles and shrugs, which Derek decides to accept for an answer. Derek holds the milk carton over his coffee cup for a moment, shaking out the few drops that Chris left when he drained it onto his cereal. Then he sighs, and spoons in sugar. He cannot enjoy black coffee unsweetened, even though he has officially given up sugar. He sits down across the table from Chris, pulling the ashtray over to his side and noticing that Chris has already helped himself to a cigarette from the pack he left beside the kettle the night before.

"Wow," says Derek, studying the packet. "You've left me a cigarette. How kind."

Chris tilts his head modestly as if at a compliment. "Any time." Then he accepts another cigarette with a quick glance at the clock on the cooker. "Ta."

"So how is She Who Must Be Obeyed these days?"

Chris leans back in his chair, cautiously welcoming the lack of reproach in his father's tone. He shakes his head. "Pretty much in control. Busy. Knackered. You know, same as ever."

"Is she still seeing that awful what's-his-name. The bookie?"

"Will. His name's Will. Yep, he's still around. He seems really good for her."

Derek inhales deeply, saying nothing. With a noise like a needle scraped across vinyl, the radio zips into a furious jingle announcing the hourly headlines. The moment for Chris to offer an apology slips past, and the DJ starts to rattle off the state of the world in seven second soundbites. Christopher stands up with what Derek recognizes as an unnecessary clatter of his chair on the tiled floor.

"Sorry, Dad, I've got to get a move on. Stacks to get through this week."

Derek tries to visualize stacks of graphic design, imagining bales of coloured paper, towers of floppy disks. "Will you be in tonight, do you think?"

Chris looks hard at the clock. "No, I'm going out. See you late-ish, maybe." He is already hooking his donkey jacket down off the back of the door when Derek says:

"Chris? If you are going to be out all night, you must let me know. I don't mind at all, as long as I know. And it would be civilized to mention it next time you're going away for the whole weekend. It's just not reasonable. I don't want to sound like your mother, but."

Chris stands with his back to the kitchen, one hand on the door handle, his jacket clenched in the other. There is a strange, tense moment where it looks as if Chris will turn round and face his father. But then he opens the back door, turning briefly to silhouette against the bright brickwork of the garage before disappearing.

Derek switches off the radio. He sits for a moment in the silence, hearing occasional high-pitched squeals from the effervescent twins next door. He knows very little about his son, he realizes.

When Eve and Derek split up, Chris was twelve and he naturally went to live with his mother. They made an effort, all three of them, and people often pointed out how wonderful they were; friends held Derek up as an example of how divorce needn't mean losing your children. Eve insisted that 'her boys' should spend virtually every weekend together. Yet, when Chris wanted to go to sixth-form college and came back to live with his father, Derek found himself sharing the house with an alien. He had read about mothers who were convinced their fishtank hospital babies had been switched at birth. Sometimes he wonders whether perhaps his son was switched at puberty.

With a shuffle, the post drops through the front door into the hall. Derek picks up the bills and circulars as he goes back upstairs to finish getting ready. He discards the pages of itemized calls to get to the bottom line of the telephone bill. A letter from the supermarket informs him that his loyalty card has only forty-five points on it, and was he aware of the outstanding range of offers that would be available to him once he reached two hundred? Derek cleans his teeth and shaves.

As he leaves the house, he looks in the mirror that hangs by the front door, inspecting his lips for traces of toothpaste, and the corners of his eyes for traces of sleep. He moves his face into a smile, watching the way the lines in his skin shift and deepen; crescent moons each side of his mouth, crow's-feet spreading out from his eyes. By lifting his eyebrows, he can still erase the double furrowed frown which is in danger of becoming permanently etched above the bridge of his nose. His dark, curly hair is sliced with grey and elegantly cut, short enough to be acceptable in the boardroom, long enough to respond well to wax when required.

For once, perhaps because he is running slightly late, Derek gets a seat on the Metro. A young Asian woman with sleek hair and cleverly kohled eyes moves her bag from the seat beside her to the floor so that he can sit down, completing the whole movement without lifting her eyes from the novel she is reading. She looks up, surprised, when he says thank you. The tram surges through a series of deep cuttings before pushing out over an optimistic landscape of car showrooms and DIY warehouses. He watches the swathes of rose-bay willow-herb flatten as the tram gathers speed, thinking how difficult it was to learn the name of that plant. Rose-willow-bay-herb. Willow-bay-rose-herb. Pink, straggling and defiant, it grows in tall sweeps of colour, submerging fly-tipped rubbish, shopping trolleys and polystyrene take-away cartons. It is August, and for once as hot and dry as August is supposed to be, even in Manchester. Derek's suit jacket prickles through his thin cotton shirt, and he thinks of Chris in his sweater and his heavy black donkey jacket. He cannot remember the last time he saw his son in anything brightly coloured or lightweight. He pictures a podgy toddler, in dazzling T-shirts and tiger-striped shorts. At some point Chris must have made the transition to long-limbed teenager, devilishly dishevelled in school uniform, refusing to wear his tie in any fashion other than ironically: the fat end and the bulk of it stuffed inside his shirt, leaving only a tiny, tight knot and a short skinny tail. When Chris was as young as ten or eleven, if Derek or Eve asked him to answer the phone while they dried their hands or lifted a pan off the heat, he would stand and watch it ringing, measuring with interest how long they would take to get to the phone, counting off the seconds. Derek wonders when it was exactly that Chris the adolescent had emerged, resisting his responsibilities even before they had accumulated. He sighs over his son for the second time this morning, and the woman next to him slides a glance sidelong without turning her head.

Derek looks out at the city as the tram makes the imperceptible switch from railway to roadway, leaving behind the unimpeded progress of its own uncomplicated tracks. It splices into the mainstream of traffic, tooting its breathy horn at pedestrians and traffic-lights, stop-starting and jolting the last half mile to St Peter's Square.

There was a time when Derek would have driven to work. When he first opted for a Head Office desk job, with a monthly salary unaffected by varying rates of commission, he stewed in stationary lanes with the best of them. Ticking over in traffic is fine for a while, and Derek remembers when it used to be part of the game: a trembling anticipation of speed to come, power reined in, just waiting for a glimpse of open motorway. But when an hour of snail-pace progress into town is rewarded by nothing more exhilarating than the queue for an NCP multi-storey, there seems little point to it. Soon, the frustration of inner-city commuting was too much for him; too hard a reminder of how driving used to be.

When Derek was first repping, driving was his favourite adrenaline boost; he lived for the thrill of tearing around the country in better cars than he could ever afford to buy, and justified excessive speeds and distances in the name of competitiveness. He was good at selling and good at driving. His sales figures were the milometer that showed how far he had come. The road, dotted with new targets and new product launches, stretched out ahead of him as far as he cared to look.

With his bare-faced grin, Derek had no trouble winning the confidence of receptionists and secretaries. He would woo them with intelligent questions, and ask for tips about their employers over lunches without strings. When they told him he was different from other reps, he would smile and shrug, and find out when the other reps were due to call and what tricks they had up their sleeves. Sometimes he would interrupt his rivals' meetings, swooping into town from the motorway, purring into car parks uninvited and walking in on them mid-pitch.

Until he was twenty-six, his life was devoted to the road.

There was nothing quite like the surge and swing of a slip road, dipping a wing into the bend, feeling the pull of the curve in his gut. He remembers weeks of driving in the sun, his elbow on the edge of an open window, singing aloud. His cigarettes tucked up above the sunshade, his stereo outfacing the rumble of articulated lorries as he ducked between them, he would cut straight through to the outside lane, aiming for ninety miles an hour.

He was already married by then, of course; Chris had just found his feet and lost his volume control. Eve was at home, absorbed in her toddler group and nappies, he supposed. On Friday nights, when he was still high and wide-eyed from driving, they would get a baby-sitter and go to a film or to a club like the Kasbar. They would sit around and smoke and maybe dance. Derek would tell people he sold drugs, watching their faces intently before telling them he meant aspirin and corn plasters. Much later, when he had moved from Newcastle and pharmaceuticals to Manchester and power tools, Eve told him she only went out because he wanted to. She had hated it, feeling old among school-aged girls in clumpy shoes, keeping her left hand out of sight with its wedding ring.

On Saturdays, Derek and Eve would stay in, playing house. If any of his friends were around, he might go to the pub, but Derek would just as soon stay in. On Sunday, he might get the AA maps out to plan a diversion around roadworks encountered the previous week.

It was after just such a cosy, recuperative weekend that Derek had his accident. Eve and Chris had waved him off on his daily adventure. He had a full tank of petrol, and the day's calls memorized as red and blue veins from the map. Derek was headed south-east, to the edge of Teeside, and the sun was in his eyes. He took one hand off the wheel to flick the sunshade down. When his cigarette packet dropped out into his lap, his attention followed it, just a glance to see where it fell. Just a reflex.

Derek doesn't often tell the story any more. He knows the shivering windscreen split a bright sky into brittle red splinters like tinsel, but when he closes his eyes to recall it, the colours have faded in much the same way as fabric fades the more you wash it. After the crash, he found the colour of life on the road had paled. The rainbow arching over the motorway, the yellow and green flashing fields, the neon-red service stations, all of them were bleached out by the bright white hospital glare in which he awoke.

The tram pulls alongside the raised platform, with its metallic shelters and ticket machines glinting in the sun, and the woman sitting beside him gets up. She leans forward to pick up her bag from the floor and a dark, slightly peppery scent is driven out from the cleavage of her cotton blouse by the movement. Derek breathes it in, recognising either *Opium* or *Poison*, and is tempted for a moment to ask her which it is. His own shirt collar is loose, two buttons open. His tie lies coiled at the bottom of his briefcase, midnight-blue silk shot through with threads of gold and turquoise.

Silk Tie

"Eve, you can *have* the sodding piano."

Derek lowers his forehead to the desk, tapping his brow on the cool mahogany edge for the benefit of his secretary, who is hovering just inside the open door. "Now I have to go. Have to. Ring me tonight. Okay, I'll ring you. Bye. Yes. Bye." He drops the receiver back on to the phone with a quick flick of his wrist, as if it is red hot. Spreading his fingers wide, he turns to Rachel.

"I'm sorry."

"It's just that everybody's in there already." She glances up at the clock, a plain stainless steel disk with three hands and no numerals, that gleams above the door. He fishes in his briefcase for his tie, looping it round the back of his upturned collar, and fastening up his top button. He has left his shirt open-necked all morning in a vain attempt to ventilate his armpits. The synthetic padding of his chair is clammy with moisture from his body, and the shirt is sticking to the small of his back. With the window closed, the room is stiflingly hot, but with it open, he cannot hear himself think and telephone conversation is impossible over the traffic noise.

Derek takes the smooth silk between his fingers, wrapping one end twice round the other and slipping it through to make a neat bulb. Tugging the knot into place, he flips his shirt collar down again with his thumbs, and looks down to check the length and flatness of the tails. The slight sparkle of the material contains a touch of glamour that is lacking from his tired wool trousers and plain cotton shirt, and the tie soothes his irritation at not having his better suit with him.

"I think we'd better get a move on," says Rachel.

When Derek inherited Rachel, everyone expected a stormy relationship. Her efficiency is well respected, but Derek has heard it used against her, as if efficiency is somehow a character defect in one so pretty. In some quarters she is even credited with hastening Derek's predecessor into his stress-related early retirement. Having spent days simply sorting through the shambolic paperwork left behind in the office, Derek suspects that Rachel's toughness was necessitated by the sheer sloppiness of her former boss. It is largely thanks to Rachel that he has settled in to his new role so easily, and he is the first to acknowledge her contribution. In the six months of Derek's tenure as new business director, Rachel has thrived on the levels of autonomy and responsibility he has willingly handed over to her.

Together, they make a hasty but late entrance into the conference room. Derek notices how all eyes turn to them, inevitably connecting them in their lateness, and he sees Rachel blush although it's not her fault. Rachel is very sensitive to what she calls 'bad vibes', and there has been an excess of atmosphere in the building this morning. She was just saying so to Derek, when Keith popped his head round the door to announce an unscheduled lunchtime meeting of the Board. Rachel pulled one eyebrow up under her straight platinum fringe. "See?"

Derek himself had noticed a subdued air to the *good weekend?* questions of the morning, but had put it down initially to his own domestic preoccupations. He is all too aware of his tendency to *project*, as Eve would put it, accusing him of ascribing his own moods to those around him. He notes with some satisfaction that this time Eve would have been wrong: the tension in the boardroom is palpable.

As Derek slides a chair across the carpet for Rachel, Keith interrupts from the head of the table:

"Oh, Rachel, there's really no need for you to give up your lunch break. Thanks anyway."

Rachel throws a sharp glance at Derek, then turns on her heel in an aloof and elegant way that he admires intensely. How she manages to communicate utter disdain with no more than a slight stiffening of her neck and shoulders is marvellous to him. He smiles as she makes her exit, leaving the room only half-filled by the board of directors.

Derek keeps the chair, positioning it wide of the conference table, leaving himself room to stretch out his legs and push himself back into the black leather slings that serve for seat and backrest. He feels the slight bounce of the tubular steel frame; flexing his ankles is enough to rock the chair in tiny movements. This spacious room is air-conditioned and pleasantly cool after his own office. The traffic noise from three floors below is muted, and the horizontal slats of the blinds reflect like chocolate ripples in the surface of the conference table. Keith is talking again:

"So confidentiality is essential, I don't think I need to say. Derek?" He passes to Derek a copy of the report that the others are already reading. It comes from hand to hand, the length of the table, down the line of bowed heads and shuffling papers. A direct line of descent, thinks Derek, with Keith Wilkinson there at the top, where he has reigned as managing director for fifteen years. Whenever he sees Keith, with his thin, white hair wispy over his domed head, Derek wonders how much longer he intends going on. He ought to be retiring soon, but the subject remains taboo except in the pub, and Derek avoids that particular forum for political manoeuvring whenever possible. The question hanging over Keith is one of succession, and in Rachel's memorable phrase: it's not exactly a beauty contest.

Beside Keith sits David Atherton, marketing director, who always introduces himself as 'call-me-Dave,' as if to make a special friend of everyone. Eternally thirty-something, he has sharp edges under his easygoing manner. Next to him sits Rob, with his woolly hair and jovial chins, who not only controls but actually seems to understand finance. Bypassing Katherine Stott, personnel director, the document comes to Derek via Hugh Ridley, Sales Director for the North-West Region. Derek sees the way Hugh glances at the report before he hands it on to Derek, just to make sure it is identical to his own copy. Hugh's thin face is twitching and he is perspiring despite the air-conditioning: his thick-framed glasses are in danger of slipping off his nose.

Derek glances at the report, which has clearly been prepared in a hurry: the two sheets of A4 paper are stapled askew. As he takes in the first paragraph, he stops rocking and sits forward in his chair.

It takes him three minutes to read the information in the report, then he rises and goes over to the fridge that stands in the corner of the room. Taking a Coke from the stack, feeling the drops of condensation slide under his fingers and track down the sides of the bottle, he breaks the silence. "Anyone else?"

In the ensuing activity of passing round drinks, they all have the chance to absorb what they have read under the bold-printed heading: **Universal Homestores**. Even Dave Atherton's affable manner is dampened by the news that the company's biggest account, the cornerstone of their whole power tools strategy, has suddenly and unexpectedly been lost.

"Does anyone know how the hell this can have happened?" Keith Wilkinson brings the meeting to order, with a cough and a gesture of empty hands. Hugh looks down at the table-top; with one finger he is tracing little x's in the thin, tubular ring of water that has condensed from his Orangina bottle. Universal is, or was, the jewel in his crown.

"What are we doing, here?" asks Derek suddenly. "Trying to find a scapegoat, or trying to sort out the mess?"

Keith continues: "I think we all know whose responsibility the Universal account was. Don't we, Hugh. I just hope you've got a bloody good explanation. If this is part of some master strategy, now is the time to let us all in on it."

Hugh Ridley's moment of crisis passes. He smears away the moisture on the table with the flat of his hand, then wipes his hand on his knee. He is red, and his eyes seem to have shrunk at the edges. Katherine, her face contorted with sympathy for his predicament, opens her mouth as if she has something to say, but Hugh gets there first. Tapping the report accusingly, he looks up and addresses the window.

"This. . . is just as much of a shock to me as it is to you. But I do know why we might have lost this account. I have a fair idea. Personalities are everything at this level, and the new buyer at Universal is. . . not *our type*. Not an excuse, I know. But we maybe needed to change tactics. Sooner."

"Rather than later," adds Keith, heavily.

"Surely it's never too late." Katherine tries to brighten the tone, and Derek is glad she is there. She brings a note of incorrigible optimism to this over-serious grey-templed board, despite her forlorn dress sense and unvaryingly drab hair. Derek supposes that she must have a rosier image of herself than the one the world sees, since she makes so little effort to improve it, and he sees in this an indication of her philosophy. For Katherine, nothing is ever as bad as you think it is, and Derek has heard her fire people, making it sound like exactly the kind of marvellous opportunity they were waiting for.

Derek tunes back in to the debacle when he hears his own name mentioned. It is up to him, he learns, to save Universal.

"After all, as it's no longer an existing account," spits Keith, his watery eyes fixed on Hugh, "that makes it New Business. Right?"

Derek wonders briefly whether his role as saviour of the universe will entitle him to wear a blue lycra body stocking and red cape, or whether he will at least be allowed to wear a big red S on his chest, but saves these observations for Rachel She will see the funny side in a way that the pale Hugh Ridley might not.

"Could you give me the contact?" Derek asks, as gently as he can. Hugh reels it off without hesitation, a name and a phone number. A woman's name, Derek notices, searching for a pen. Quite unusual in garden and electrical. He is avoiding Hugh's venomous look when his hand closes on a smooth cylinder in the pocket of his jacket, and turning the report over to note down the name, Erica something, Derek takes out what he thinks is a biro, but which is, in fact, a Christian Dior russet brown lip pencil.

Additional Contributors

Sue Hubbard is a poet and an art critic for *Time Out* and *The New Statesman*. Her poems have appeared in anthologies such as *Klaonica* (Bloodaxe) and *In the Gold of Flesh* (Women's Press). She has won a number of prizes and published two pamphlets of poetry. Her first collection, *Everything Begins with the Skin*, is published by Enitharmon. She has done the MA part-time: her story *A Sprig of Basil* therefore appeared in the 1995 anthology *Harlequinned*. She is working on her first full novel.

Chris Copin (cover design) is an Erasmus student at Norfolk School of Art & Design. He comes from Normandy, and studied graphic design and silk screen printing at Lisieux. He likes cats, black clothes and 60's TV programmes especially *The Avengers*.

Emma Hargrave (copy editing) lives in Leeds. She is a freelance copy editor. Her clients include Faber & Faber and Creation Press.

Richard Johnson (layout) lives in deepest Norfolk with his wife and kids. He is a freelance designer.